Introduction to Management Science

FOURTH EDITION

David W. Pentico
Duquense University

Robert A. Russell
University of Tulsa

Timothy L. Urban
University of Tulsa

STUDY GUIDE

Introduction to Management Science FOURTH EDITION

Thomas M. Cook
American Airlines, Inc.

Robert A. Russell
The University of Tulsa

PRENTICE HALL, Englewood Cliffs, New Jersey 07632

Editorial/production supervision: *Kris Ann Cappelluti*
Manufacturing buyer: *Peter Havens*

Printed in the United States of America

10 9 8 7 6 5 4 3 2

ISBN: 0-13-486333-X

Prentice-Hall International (UK) Limited, *London*
Prentice-Hall of Australia Pty. Limited, *Sydney*
Prentice-Hall Canada Inc., *Toronto*
Prentice-Hall Hispanoamericana, S.A., *Mexico*
Prentice-Hall of India Private Limited, *New Delhi*
Prentice-Hall of Japan, Inc., *Tokyo*
Simon & Schuster Asia Pte. Ltd., *Singapore*
Editora Prentice-Hall do Brasil, Ltda., *Rio de Janeiro*

Contents

To the Student

What is a study guide and how should you use it?

This study guide is a collection of summaries, vocabulary, supplements, and testing devices that have been written specifically to help you develop a better understanding of and greater confidence in your ability to work with the techniques of Management Science as presented in Introduction to Management Science, Fourth Edition, by Thomas M. Cook and Robert A. Russell.

The chapters of this book parallel the chapters of the text. The study guide chapters contain, in general, the same kinds of materials, each aimed at providing you with a different and specific kind of experience to help you learn the text material better.

The Main Points section is a summary of the ideas and techniques discussed in the chapter, presenting the material in the same order in which it is covered in the text. In some cases, where we felt that there was a useful alternative explanation or some additional material that would help you, we included that also. You can use this section to refresh your memory after you have read the chapter, as a preview of what will be discussed, or for both purposes.

Suggested Readings are given for most chapters. In some cases, classic works not listed in the text, are provided. The real purpose, however, is to provide you with a short list of application articles selected from the literature. These have been chosen, generally, with the idea that they will give you some insight into the kinds of applications for which the techniques are used, will be readable, and will not duplicate the scenarios illustrated at the start of the text chapters. Most of these articles come from Interfaces because it is the most readable journal in Management Science. Other journals in which you will regularly find application articles include:

Computers and Operations Research
Decision Sciences
European Journal of Operational Research
IIE Transactions
INFOR - Information Systems and Operational Research
International Journal of Production Research
Journal of Financial and Quantitative Analysis
Journal of Operations Management
Journal of the Operational Research Society
Management Science
Networks
Omega - International Journal of Management Science
Operations Research
Production and Inventory Management Journal
Society for Industrial and Applied Mathematics Review
Simulation
Transportation Science

There are many other journals that occasionally contain articles that would be classified as Management Science.

Key Terms is a vocabulary section in which you are to match the principal new vocabulary of the chapter with definitions that reflect their meanings in that context. Being able to speak the language of Management Science is essential for developing a good understanding of its techniques and their application.

The Solved Problems section illustrates key problem types and a full explanation of their solution. These are designed to provide more examples and further explanation beyond the text.

The Review Exercises are problem sets to help you test your ability to develop models and use the techniques discussed for solving them. Some are routine and provide an alternative and additional practice relative to the text. A few are more difficult and will stretch your imagination. They are marked with an asterisk (*). If you cannot solve them, don't be discouraged. We hope that when you see their answers you will understand them and, therefore, will grow a little in your understanding of Management Science.

The last section of each chapter is a Chapter Test, a series of multiple choice questions. Most questions test your understanding of the concepts of the chapter and its vocabulary. A few are numerical problems that test your ability to use the techniques.

How you can best use this study guide depends, largely, on the orientation of the course you are taking. If the focus of your course is entirely on the mathematical models and their solution, pay particular attention to the Solved Problems, Review Exercises, and the quantitative questions in the Chapter Tests. If your course also puts heavy emphasis on ideas, concepts, and the use of the models in practice, you should find the other sections of equal use.

Best of luck to you as you study this material. We hope that what we have tried to do here will make it somewhat easier for you.

David W. Pentico
Robert A. Russell
Timothy L. Urban

Introduction to Management Science

FOURTH EDITION

CHAPTER ONE

INTRODUCTION

MAIN POINTS

1. Management science, also known as operations research, is the discipline devoted to studying, developing, and using procedures to help in making organizational decisions.

2. By following the scientific method, management science provides a rational, systematic way of making decisions, thus increasing the chances of making better decisions.

3. Although various operations research techniques date to the early 1900's, management science as a recognized discipline dates to World War II when interdisciplinary teams were assembled to work on military problems. The main impetuses to acceptance by business and other non-military users came in the late 1940's with the development by Dantzig of linear programming and the invention of the electronic computer.

4. As management science has matured there has been greater emphasis placed on less well-defined problems and on the interface with management information systems, leading to the merging of MIS and OR/MS in decision support systems.

5. The five steps of the scientific method are: observation, problem definition, hypothesis formulation, experimentation, and verification. In real-world, as opposed to laboratory, situations, experimentation and verification pose special problems. Thus, most management science experiments are conducted on mathematical models, usually expressed as computer programs.

6. A key concept in management science is the systems approach, considering the system as a whole and the interaction of its various parts. The focus is on optimizing overall system performance. Optimization of subsystems can lead to suboptimization of the whole.

7. The use of multidisciplinary teams enhances problem definition and analysis by bringing a variety of perspectives to bear on the problem.

8. A model is a simplified representation or abstraction of reality. They can be used for estimating cause-effect relationships and the interactions between variables.

9. An iconic model looks like what it represents. An analog model uses property replacement such as distance for time in a graph. A symbolic or mathematical model uses symbols to represent system components and their attributes and mathematical equations, inequalities, and logical relationships to express the relationships among the components and their attributes.

1

10. In developing a mathematical model the analyst must define variables, including both those representing the decisions and the uncontrollable features, an objective function to be used in measuring the effectiveness of proposed solutions, and constraints.

11. The basic steps in the OR/MS approach are: problem formulation to recognize the real problem and not just the symptoms; model development, both as to general type and the specific parameters and relationships; model solution or manipulation; establishment of controls over the model's use; and implementation, recognizing human factors and behavioral aspects.

12. Management science interacts with all functional areas of business, both in terms of getting information, policies, and guidance from the areas and in providing models for the solution of problems in the areas.

13. Management science techniques can be classified according to the nature of the decision environment as: deterministic, in which everything relevant is known; stochastic, in which some variables have probability distributions; and uncertain.

SUGGESTED READINGS

One of the earliest, and still one of the best, treatments of the concepts, issues in, and philosophy of operations research/management science is:

Churchman, C. W., R. L. Ackoff, and E. L. Arnoff, Introduction to Operations Research (New York: John Wiley & Sons, Inc., 1957).

There have been many books and articles written on the art of modeling and the use of models in decision making. Two that the author has found to be of particular interest are:

Little, J. D. C., "Models and Managers: The Concept of a Decision Calculus," Management Science, v. 16, n. 8 (April 1970), pp. B466-B485.

Morris, W. T., "On the Art of Modeling," Management Science, v. 13, n. 12 (August 1967), pp. B707-B717.

Robert Machol wrote a series of twelve columns entitled "Principles of Operations Research" that appeared in various issues of Interfaces between May 1974 (v. 4, n. 3) and May 1978 (v. 8, n. 3). They discuss many of the serious issues in using OR/MS techniques in a somewhat humorous manner.

R. E. D. (Gene) Woolsey has, since the May 1974 (v. 4, n. 3) issue of Interfaces, written or edited "The Fifth Column." This is, again, a humorous approach to many of the serious issues involved in practicing Operations Research, citing case examples to reinforce his points.

A series of applications-oriented articles, "OR Practice," have been published since the November-December 1985 (v. 33, n. 6) issue of Operations Research. These papers are intended to appeal to the OR practitioner as well as the researcher.

KEY TERMS

Match each term with the appropriate definition from below.

Terms

_I_	1. algorithm	_C_	8. objective function
_L_	2. analog model	_K_	9. operations research
_E_	3. constraint	_D_	10. optimization
_F_	4. deterministic	_M_	11. scientific method
_B_	5. iconic model	_A_	12. stochastic
_H_	6. management science	_G_	13. systems approach
_J_	7. mathematical model		

Definitions

A. Characterizes an environment in which variables have probability distributions.

B. A model that looks like what it represents.

C. An expression that measures the desirability of a proposed solution.

D. Seeking the best answer.

E. A limitation on the values that decision variables may take on.

F. Characterizes an environment in which everything relevant is known.

G. Analysis which recognizes the interactions among the various aspects of and components of a system.

H. The application of rational, structured analysis to organizational decision making.

I. A step-by-step approach to solving a problem or model.

J. A model in which relationships are represented by mathematical expressions.

K. Another name for management science.

L. A model based on property substitution.

M. The five-step process that serves as the basis for OR/MS.

SOLVED PROBLEM

A firm can sell 2,000 units of a product for a particular customer at a price of $90 per unit. The product would require the purchase of capital equipment costing $10,000, and the variable cost of producing a unit is $60. The firm has enough excess capacity to produce the product.

a. In solving this decision problem, what is the relevant objective or criterion?

b. What alternatives exist for the decision maker's consideration?

c. Construct a general model expressing the relevant expense calculations for arbitrary costs.

d. Construct a simple decision rule to select the best alternative.

Solution

a. A relevant criterion would be to maximize profit.

b. The simple alternatives are to (1) produce the product for the customer or (2) reject the order.

c. Let f = the fixed costs of producing the product
       v = the variable cost per unit
   The general expense model could be stated as:

$$E = f + 2000v$$

d. The revenue calculation can be expressed as:

$$R = 2000p \qquad \text{where } p = \text{profit per unit}$$

The decision rule can be stated as:

produce if $R > E$, otherwise reject the order

For $p = 90$, $f = 10000$, and $v = 60$, we have

$$R = 2,000(90) = 180,000$$
$$E = 10,000 + 2,000(60) = 130,000$$
$$R > E$$

Therefore produce unless there are other more profitable uses of the production resources

REVIEW EXERCISES

1. The Whittaker Corp. is considering the introduction of a new product. To install the equipment and pay for other fixed costs will cost an estimated $500,000 per year. The variable unit costs are projected to be $4.50 per unit. They expect to be able to sell the product for $7.00 per unit. How many units will Whittaker have to sell per year before it makes a profit?

2. The Chambers Machine Shop has four lathe jobs to be done and four lathes available on which to do them.   Due to differences in lathe capabilities and the specific requirements of the jobs, there are differences in the expected times required for each lathe-job combination.   These times are shown in the table.

	Lathe			
Job	1	2	3	4
A	19	5	16	6
B	9	17	5	10
C	10	12	15	14
D	6	14	9	8

Which job should be assigned to which lathe (one job per lathe, one lathe per job) to minimize the total time to do all four jobs?

3. A company has $1,000,000 to invest in capital projects for the coming year.   Each project costs a certain amount and is expected to provide a certain return, both shown in the table.   A project must be adopted in its entirety or not at all.   Which projects should the company undertake to maximize the total expected benefit?   Any money not used for projects can be invested at 10 percent interest for the year.

Project	Cost	Return
1	$100,000	$ 240,000
2	600,000	1,300,000
3	450,000	900,000
4	500,000	950,000
5	275,000	495,000
6	330,000	495,000

CHAPTER TEST

1. In conducting an OR/MS study, the first step is to:
   a. collect data.
   b. identify the problem.
   c. develop a model.
   d. perform a validation study.

2. A model is:
   a. an abstraction from reality.
   b. useful for analyzing complex problems.
   c. helpful in determining cause-effect relationships.
   d. all of the above.

3. Which of the following is not a characteristic of the OR/MS approach?
   a. It is based on the scientific method.
   b. It involves the use of models.
   c. It guarantees solutions to all problems.
   d. It is systems oriented.

4. OR/MS techniques are now used in:
   a. business organizations.
   b. government organizations.
   c. health care organizations.
   d. all of the above.

5. Most OR/MS studies involve the use of computers because:
   a. there is a great deal of numerical calculation.
   b. computers make results more believable.
   c. computers are necessary for representing mathematical models.
   d. computers are fun to work with.

6. All decision models contain:
   a. stochastic variables.
   b. constraints.
   c. decision variables.
   d. all of the above.

7. When a model contains probability distributions for some variables it is called:
   a. deterministic.
   b. stochastic.
   c. uncertain.
   d. none of the above.

8. Real-world experimentation is difficult in management science studies because:
   a. it is difficult to control the environment.
   b. the result of a mistake could mean organizational failure.
   c. the time to implement and test changes may be too long.
   d. all of the above.

9. A model that involves replacing the properties of one system by those of another is called:
   a. a symbolic model.
   b. an analog model.
   c. an iconic model.
   d. a mathematical model.

10. The component of a mathematical decision model that measures the effectiveness of proposed solutions is the:
    a. decision variables.
    b. objective function.
    c. constraints.
    d. non-negativity requirement.

ANSWER KEY

Key Terms

1. I	3. E	5. B	7. J	9. K	11. M	13. G
2. L	4. F	6. H	8. C	10. D	12. A	

Review Exercises

1. This is an example of a standard break-even analysis problem. The problem is to find the sales quantity, X, that will equate the total production and revenue costs.

$$\begin{aligned}
\text{Production Cost} &= \text{Revenue} \\
500{,}000 + 4.50X &= 7.00X \\
500{,}000 &= 2.50X \\
X &= 200{,}000
\end{aligned}$$

They will make a profit if they sell over 200,000 units per year.

2. One way of solving this problem is brute force. There are $4! = 24$ different ways of assigning jobs to machines. Each of the 24 can be evaluated to see how much time it will take. While possible for a small problem such as this one, it would be impractical to use this method for a large problem. Even with only 10 jobs and machines there are over 3.6 million possibilities. As the problem becomes larger, the number of possibilities increases dramatically.

For larger problems the OR/MS model known as the Assignment Problem, discussed in Chapter 6, can be used.

The optimal solution to this problem calls for the following machine-job assignments:

$$1 - C, \quad 2 - A, \quad 3 - B, \quad 4 - D$$

which has a cost of $10 + 5 + 5 + 8 = 28$.

3. This problem is similar to the knapsack problem in the text except that the extra money (weight) available can be invested for a return. If we define:

$$X_i = \begin{cases} 1 \text{ if project } i \text{ is adopted, } i = 1,\dots,6 \\ 0 \text{ if not} \end{cases}$$

and X_7 = the amount in 1000's invested at 10 percent

Then our problem is:

maximize $240X_1 + 1300X_2 + 900X_3 + 950X_4 + 495X_5 + 495X_6 + 1.1X_7$

subject to: $100X_1 + 600X_2 + 450X_3 + 500X_4 + 275X_5 + 330X_6 + X_7 = 1{,}000$

$$X_1, X_2, X_3, X_4, X_5, X_6 = 0 \text{ or } 1; \quad X_7 \geq 0$$

One way to solve this problem is to try all possible combinations of projects that cost less, in total, than $1,000,000, evaluating the objective function value for each feasible set. The solution obtained by doing this is:

$$X_1 = X_2 = X_5 = 1, \quad X_3 = X_4 = X_6 = 0, \quad X_7 = 25$$

and the value of the objective function is $2,062,500.

7

Chapter Test

1. b	3. c	5. a	7. b	9. d
2. d	4. d	6. c	8. d	10. b

CHAPTER TWO

LINEAR PROGRAMMING: FORMULATION AND APPLICATIONS

MAIN POINTS

1. Linear Programming (LP) problems are generally allocation problems of one of two types. One type involves the allocation of scarce resources among alternative uses in such a way as to maximize the value obtained from their use. An example would be a product mix problem, determining how much of each of several products to manufacture so as to maximize the total contribution to profit and overhead while staying within available resource limits. The second type is the allocation of the efforts to meet a set of needs or requirements among alternative ways of satisfying them, the objective being to minimize the cost. An example is the diet problem, selecting a minimum cost food combination that will satisfy nutritional requirements.

2. LP is a special case of the general field of mathematical programming, which involves the selection of values for decision variables that will optimize the value of an objective function subject to satisfying a set of constraints expressed as equations or inequalities.

3. The majority of applications of LP can be classified into one of five categories: blending, product-mix, physical distribution and assignment, production scheduling and inventory planning, and purchasing.

4. LP is a procedure for maximizing or minimizing a linear objective function subject to a set of linear equality or inequality constraints.

5. Formulating an LP model involves the specification of three model components. <u>Decision variables</u> provide the answers to the problem being investigated. The <u>objective function</u> measures the effectiveness of a solution, which is a set of values for the decision variables that satisfies a series of <u>constraints</u>. The constraints specify the limitations in the problem, such as scarce resources, requirements to be satisfied, and nonnegativity of variables. The specification of the objective function and constraints involves the determination of parameter values for the constants in the expressions.

6. The formulation of a successful LP model is a six step process:
   a. Understand the problem.
   b. Define the decision variables.
   c. Select a numerical measure of effectiveness (the objective) for choosing among solutions.
   d. Express the objective as a linear expression involving the decision variables and constraints.
   e. Identify the constraints and express them as linear equations or inequalities involving the decision variables.
   f. Determine values for all parameters by collecting data or making estimates.

7. Besides nonnegativity, which is assumed in most LP problems and is handled automatically by the standard solution procedures, there are four general types of constraints.
   a. Resource limitations specify upper bounds on the amounts available of scarce resources such as people, money, materials, or time.
   b. Requirements or standards may need to be satisfied, such as nutrition, demands, or cash flow requirements. These may be either upper or lower limits.
   c. Balancing constraints establish relationships among variable sets. Examples are that production must at least meet sales or that one kind of investment cannot exceed another.
   d. Definitional equations establish the value of one variable as a function of others. For example, ending inventory equals beginning inventory plus production minus use.

8. The direct use of LP is limited by its assumptions. First, it is assumed that there is a single goal or objective to be maximized or minimized. Second is determinism. It is assumed that all relevant parameter values are known with _certainty_. Third is _linearity_. It is assumed that all relationships in the model - the objective function and all constraints - can be expressed as linear expressions. This implies two things: _proportionality_ and _additivity_. Finally, we assume _divisibility_. This means that a decision variable can take on any real number value within the range given by the constraints. If, in practice, the decision variables must really be limited to integer values, LP can be used for approximations, but an optimum solution requires the use of integer linear programming, a topic in Chapter 9.

9. Although small LP problems can be solved by hand or with the aid of a calculator, real-world problems often involve hundreds or thousands of variables and constraints and require a computer and special software for their solution.

SUGGESTED READINGS

Selected applications are:

Arnold, L. R. and D. Botkin, "Portfolios to Satisfy Damage Judgments: A Linear Programming Approach," _Interfaces_, v. 8, n. 2 (April 1978), pp. 38-42.

Brosch, L. C. , et al., "Boxcars, Linear Programming, and the Sleeping Kitten," _Interfaces_, v. 10, n. 6 (December 1980), pp. 53-61.

Byrd, J. and L. T. Moore, "The Application of a Product Mix Linear Programming Model in Corporate Policy Making," _Management Science_, v. 24, n. 13 (September 1978), pp. 1342-1350.

Carino, H. F. and C. H. Lenoir, Jr., "Optimizing Wood Procurement in Cabinet Manufacturing," _Interfaces_, v. 18, n. 2 (March-April 1988), pp. 10-19.

Gabella, A. and W. Pearce, "Telephone Sales Manpower Planning at Qantas," _Interfaces_, v. 9, n. 3 (June 1979), pp. 1-9.

Hilal, S. S. and W. Erickson, "Matching Supplies to Save Lives: Linear Programming the Production of Heart Valves," Interfaces, v. 11, n. 6 (December 1981), pp. 48-56.

Woolsey, R. E. D., "A Novena to St. Jude, or Four Edifying Case Studies in Mathematical Programming," Interfaces, v. 4, n. 1 (November 1973), pp. 32-39.

KEY TERMS

Match each term with the appropriate definition below.

Terms

__D__ 1. additivity

__I__ 2. blending

__G__ 3. constraint

__K__ 4. decision variable

__A__ 5. divisibility

__M__ 6. linearity

__H__ 7. linear programming

__J__ 8. objective function

__B__ 9. parameters

__L__ 10. physical distribution

__F__ 11. product mix

__E__ 12. proportionality

__C__ 13. sensitivity analysis

Definitions

A. The property of LP that permits a variable to take on any real value in the allowable range.

B. The constants in the objective function and constraints.

C. A technique for exploring the effects of changing parameters over a range of values.

D. The assumption in LP that the effect of a combination of variable values is simply the sum of their individual effects.

E. A type of LP problem that involves determining how much of each of a set of products to make to maximize gain subject to resource limits.

F. The assumption of LP that says that if you double, triple, etc. the value of a variable you also double, triple, etc. its total effect on cost, contribution, or resource use.

G. An equality or inequality that specifies a limitation on the possible values of decision variables.

H. A procedure for maximizing the value of a linear objective function subject to a set of linear constraints.

I.   A type of LP problem that involves determining how to mix components together so as to satisfy certain requirements at minimum cost.

J.   A mathematical expression that measures the effectiveness of a set of decision variable values.

K.   A variable whose value, when solved for optimally, provides an answer to a question addressed by the model.

L.   A type of LP problem that involves the shipment of goods from supply points to use points in such a way as to meet all demands, stay within available supplies, and minimize shipping costs.

M.   The assumption of LP that implies proportionality and additivity of effects for both the objective function and the constraints.

SOLVED PROBLEM

A paper company produces rolls of paper used in calculators and cash registers. They produce a stock roll that is 30 feet long and 10 inches wide. To produce different final products, they must cut the stock rolls lengthwise to achieve various widths. Next month, the company has demand for 1.5 and 2.5 inch wide rolls. The production requirements are:

Roll Width	Number of Units
1.5	500
2.5	1000

The company wants to cut the minimum number of 10-inch stock rolls in order to meet demand. Formulate a linear programming model to solve the problem.

Solution

The key to modeling this problem is to determine the correct decision variables. Some students will define the decision variables as the number of 10-inch rolls to cut in 1.5 and 2.5 inch widths. However, the correct formulation requires the determination of all possible pattern cuts of the 10-inch roll. The following patterns are possible:

Cutting Pattern	1.5 inch	2.5 inch	Waste (inches)
1	6	0	1
2	5	1	0
3	3	2	0.5
4	1	3	1
5	0	4	0

To solve the problem, the decision maker needs to know how to cut the 10-inch rolls. Therefore, a decision variable is needed for each possible pattern.

Let: X_1 = number of 10-inch rolls cut into pattern 1

X_2 = number of 10-inch rolls cut into pattern 2

X_3 = number of 10-inch rolls cut into pattern 3

X_4 = number of 10-inch rolls cut into pattern 4

X_5 = number of 10-inch rolls cut into pattern 5

Since the objective is to minimize the total number of 10-inch rolls cut, the objective function can be stated as:

$$\text{minimize} \quad X_1 + X_2 + X_3 + X_4 + X_5$$

There is no stated limit on the availability of 10-inch rolls, therefore the only constraints pertain to satisfying demand. Each pattern that produces a 1.5-inch roll will be reflected in the demand constraint for 1.5-inch rolls. Thus, the two required constraints are:

$$6X_1 + 5X_2 + 3X_3 + 1X_4 \geq 500$$
$$1X_2 + 2X_3 + 3X_4 + 4X_5 \geq 1000$$
$$X_1, X_2, X_3, X_4, X_5 \geq 0$$

Note that the formulation minimizes the number of 10-inch rolls cut and not necessarily square inches of waste.

REVIEW EXERCISES

1. The Blackwell Manufacturing Co. produces two products, A and B. Each product requires time in two departments and uses some of a raw material. Product A requires 2 hours in Department T, 5 hours in Department P, and takes 6 pounds of material. Product B requires 3 hours in Department T, 6 hours in Department P, and uses 4 pounds of material. There are 30 hours available in Department T, 40 hours available in Department P, and 60 pounds of material available. A unit of Product A contributes $10 to profit and overhead; a unit of Product B contributes $12. Develop an LP model to determine what Blackwell should do.

2. The Purr-Dew Poultry Co. wants to determine how to mix the available commercial chicken feeds to meet their nutritional standards at a minimum cost. There are two feeds available, each of which contains nutrients as described in the table on the next page.

	Feed	
Nutrient	X	Y
A	1	2
B	1.5	1
C	2	2
Cost/pound	$.40	$.50

Purr-Dew requires 50 units of Nutrient A, 45 units of Nutrient B, and 80 units of Nutrient C in the feed mix. Develop an LP model to determine what Purr-Dew should do.

13

3. The Central National Bank's Trust Department has been designated as the administrator for an estate of $600,000. The trust officer put in charge of this portfolio must determine how to prudently invest the money so as to generate reasonable income.

There are five investment opportunities available for using the money. They are described in the table.

Investment	Return	Risk Factor
Stock A	.15	.05
Stock B	.20	.10
Bond D	.10	.02
Bond G	.12	.04
COD	.09	0

The guidelines that the trust officer must follow are:
   a) The weighted risk should not exceed .05.
   b) Stocks should not exceed one-half of the portfolio.
   c) There should be no more in stocks than in CODs.

Formulate an LP model to determine how to invest the money so as to maximize the return.

4. The Municipal Bus Co. drivers work eight hour shifts, starting at 3 a.m., 7 a.m., 11 a.m., 3 p.m, 7 p.m., or 11 p.m. Based on projected passenger demands, the bus company requires the following numbers of drivers by time period.

Time Period	No. of Drivers
3 a.m.- 7 a.m.	10
7 a.m.-11 a.m.	20
11 a.m.- 3 p.m.	12
3 p.m.- 7 p.m.	20
7 p.m.-11 p.m.	8
11 p.m.- 3 a.m.	4

Develop an LP model to determine how to schedule the drivers so as to minimize the total number of drivers needed while meeting all requirements.

*5. (Continuation of (4).) Suppose that drivers can work overtime, working 12 hours straight instead of only eight hours. A driver is paid $80 for a regular shift and receives an extra $60 for the extra four hours. Company policy limits the number of drivers on overtime at any time to no more than 20 percent of the total drivers at that time. Develop an LP model that will schedule the drivers at minimum cost.

6. The Charlotte Chocolate Co. produces three mixes of chocolate candies, packaged in two pound boxes. Each mix is a combination of some or all of four basic types of chocolates: cream centers, nut centers, jelly centers, and mint centers. The amount of each basic type in a mix is not firmly prescribed but is subject to certain limitations as described in the table.

14

Basic Type	Regular Mix	Deluxe	Supreme
Cream Center	≤ 30%	≤ 20%	≤ 10%
Nut Center	≤ 30%	≤ 20%	≤ 20%
Jelly Center	≥ 20%	≥ 10%	≥ 10%
Mint Center	No Limit	≥ 10%	≥ 20%

A pound of cream centers costs $1.00 to make, a pound of nut centers costs $1.25, a pound of jelly centers costs $1.40, and a pound of mint centers costs $1.70. CCC has the capacity to produce 250, 250, 150, and 75 pounds per day of the cream, nut, jelly, and mint centers, respectively. Regular mix sells for $4.00 a box, Deluxe for $4.50 a box, and Supreme for $5.00 a box. Develop an LP model to determine what CCC should do to maximize profit contribution.

7. The Miller Manufacturing Co. is developing a production plan for the next six months. Forecasted demands over the planning horizon are:

Month	Demand
1	2500
2	2200
3	2700
4	3000
5	3200
6	2400

Production capacity is 2700 units per month on regular time at a cost of $10 per unit. Overtime is available at up to 20 percent of normal time capacity at an extra $5 per unit. The product can be carried in inventory for $1 per unit per month, applied to month-end inventory. Due to space problems, there is a limit of 300 units in inventory at the end of any month. There are 100 units in inventory at the beginning of month 1 and there should be 150 units in inventory at the end of month 6. Develop an LP model to meet forecasted demands and the inventory requirement at minimum cost.

8. Big Star Brewing operates three breweries in Houston, Amarillo, and San Antonio. Per barrel production costs vary slightly at the three breweries, being $3.50 at Houston, $3.20 at Amarillo, and $3.30 at San Antonio. Big Star operates three distribution centers in addition to those at its breweries. They are at El Paso, Fort Worth, and Abilene. Transportation costs from the breweries to the distribution centers, in cost per barrel are:

	To		
From	EP	FW	Ab
Ho	1.60	.70	1.00
Am	1.00	.90	.75
SA	1.50	.80	.70

In addition to the requirements of its own distribution center, each brewery has extra capacity, in barrels per week:

Brewery	Capacity
Ho	500
Am	600
SA	1000

The distribution centers have projected needs, in barrels per week:

Distribution Center	Requirement
EP	900
FW	600
Ab	400

Develop an LP model to determine how Big Star can meet its distribution requirements at the minimum cost.

CHAPTER TEST

1. Which of the following is <u>not</u> generally a feature of LP models?
   a. Divisibility of variables.
   b. Additivity of effects.
   c. Stochastic variables.
   d. Nonnegativity of variables.

2. Constraints in an LP problem may express:
   a. resource limits.
   b. requirements to be met.
   c. balances to be achieved.
   d. all of the above.

3. The purpose of an objective function is to:
   a. ensure that a proposed solution meets all requirements.
   b. evaluate the quality of a solution.
   c. ensure that variables are all nonnegative.
   d. ensure that the solution chosen is implementable.

4. The feature that distinguishes LP problems from other types of mathematical programming problems is:
   a. the decision variables cannot be integer.
   b. the objective function and constraints are all linear expressions.
   c. the solution procedure guarantees an optimal solution.
   d. the variables are required to be nonnegative.

5. Which of the following is <u>not</u> a correct completion for this statement? "The assumption of linearity means that:
   a. there are no interaction effects between variables.
   b. the contribution of a variable is proportional to the size of its value.
   c. a variable can take on any value in its allowable range.
   d. a variable must be nonnegative.

6. Which of the following is <u>not</u> a legitimate LP constraint?
   a. $3(A/B) + 4C \leq 6$
   b. $5A - 6B \geq 0$
   c. $-\sqrt{2}A + -\sqrt{5}B \leq 12$
   d. None are legitimate.

7. Which of the following statements is true?
   a. An LP problem optimizes a linear or nonlinear objective function subject to a set of linear constraints.
   b. In an LP problem the decisions are represented by the coefficients of the variables in the objective function.
   c. In an LP problem, the nonnegativity requirement means that coefficients cannot be negative.
   (d.) None are true.

8. If several ingredients are to be combined to produce a product that meets certain specifications in the minimum cost way, the LP model formulated would be classified as a:
   a. product mix problem.
   (b.) blending problem.
   c. assignment problem.
   d. purchasing problem.

9. If an LP problem involves allocating several scarce resources among the production of a set of alternative products in such a way as to minimize cost, the problem would be classified as a:
   (a.) product mix problem.
   b. blending problem.
   c. production scheduling and inventory planning problem.
   d. assignment problem.

10. A factory makes two products, A and B. Product A takes 3 hours in Department 1; Product B takes 2 hours in Department 1. Department 1 has 12 hours available. The LP constraint that represents this limitation is:
    a. $(1/3)A + (1/2)B \le 12$.
    b. $A + B \le 12/6$.
    (c.) $3A + 2B \le 12$.
    d. $4A + 6B \ge 1$.

ANSWER KEY

Terms

1. D	3. G	5. A	7. H	9. B	12. F	13. C
2. I	4. K	6. M	8. J	10. L	11. E	

Review Exercises

1. The problem is to determine how much to make of each product.

   Define: A = the number of units of Product A to make
            B = the number of units of Product B to make

   The objective is to maximize total profit contribution.

   maximize $10A + 12B$
   subject to:

   $$2A + 6B \le 30 \quad \text{Dept. T}$$
   $$5A + 4B \le 40 \quad \text{Dept. P}$$
   $$6A + 4B \le 60 \quad \text{Material}$$
   $$A, B \ge 0$$

17

2. The problem is to determine how much of each feed to blend together.

   Define: X = number of pounds of Feed X to use
            Y = number of pounds of Feed Y to use

   The objective is to minimize the total cost of meeting the nutritional standards.

   minimize   .40X + .45Y
   subject to:

   $$1X + 2Y \geq 50 \text{ Nutrient A}$$
   $$1.5X + 1Y \geq 45 \text{ Nutrient B}$$
   $$2X + 2Y \geq 80 \text{ Nutrient C}$$
   $$X, Y \geq 0$$

3. The problem is to determine how much money to invest in each of the available alternatives.

   Define: A = the amount invested in Stock A
            B = the amount invested in Stock B
            D = the amount invested in Bond D
            G = the amount invested in Bond G
            C = the amount invested in CODs

   The objective is to maximize the total return for the portfolio.

   maximize   .15A + .20B + .10D + .12G + .09C
   subject to:
   (a) $.05A + .10B + .02D + .04G \leq .05(600,000)$
   (b) $A + B \leq 300,000$
   (c) $A + B - C \leq 0$
            $A + B + D + G + C = 600,000$
            $A, B, D, G, C \geq 0$

4. The problem is to determine how many drivers should <u>start</u> work at each potential time.

   Define: X_1 = number of drivers who start at 3 a.m.

            X_2 = number of drivers who start at 7 a.m.

            X_3 = number of drivers who start at 11 a.m.

            X_4 = number of drivers who start at 3 p.m.

            X_5 = number of drivers who start at 7 p.m.

            X_6 = number of drivers who start at 11 p.m.

   Remember that a driver works 8 hours straight so he or she works the period in which he or she starts and the following period. A driver who starts in period 6 (11 p.m. - 3 a.m.) also works period 1 (3 a.m. - 7 a.m.) the next day.

   The objective is to minimize the total number of drivers scheduled.

minimize $\qquad X_1 + X_2 + X_3 + X_4 + X_5 + X_6$

subject to:

(3 a.m. - 7 a.m.) $\quad X_1 \qquad\qquad\qquad + X_6 \geqq 10$

(7 a.m. - 11 a.m.) $\quad X_1 + X_2 \qquad\qquad\qquad \geqq 20$

(11 a.m. - 3 p.m.) $\qquad\quad X_2 + X_3 \qquad\qquad \geqq 12$

(3 p.m. - 7 p.m.) $\qquad\qquad\quad X_3 + X_4 \qquad \geqq 20$

(7 p.m. - 11 p.m.) $\qquad\qquad\qquad X_4 + X_5 \quad \geqq 8$

(11 p.m. - 3 a.m.) $\qquad\qquad\qquad\qquad X_5 + X_6 \geqq 4$

all $X_i \geqq 0$

5. Now we must determine not only how many eight-hour drivers will start at each possible time, but also how many 12-hour drivers will start at each possible time.

Define: $X_1 - X_6$ as in Exercise 4, 8-hour drivers

$Y_1 - Y_6$ similarly, but 12-hour drivers

Now the drivers working at a given time fall into one of <u>five</u> groups: 8-hour drivers just starting, 8-hour drivers who are finishing, 12-hour drivers just starting, 12-hour drivers in their second four hours, and 12-hour drivers in their overtime period.

The objective is to minimize total driver cost.

minimize $\quad 80X_1 + 80X_2 + 80X_3 + 80X_4 + 80X_5 + 80X_6$
$\qquad\qquad + 140Y_1 + 140Y_2 + 140Y_3 + 140Y_4 + 140Y_5 + 140Y_6$

subject to:

The coverage requirements:

(3 a.m. - 7 a.m.) $\quad X_1 + X_6 + Y_1 + Y_5 + Y_6 \geqq 10$

(7 a.m. - 11 a.m.) $\quad X_1 + X_2 + Y_1 + Y_2 + Y_6 \geqq 20$

(11 a.m. - 3 p.m.) $\quad X_2 + X_3 + Y_1 + Y_2 + Y_3 \geqq 12$

(3 p.m. - 7 p.m.) $\quad X_3 + X_4 + Y_2 + Y_3 + Y_4 \geqq 20$

(7 p.m. - 11 p.m.) $\quad X_4 + X_5 + Y_3 + Y_4 + Y_5 \geqq 8$

(11 p.m. - 3 a.m.) $\quad X_5 + X_6 + Y_4 + Y_5 + Y_6 \geqq 4$

The overtime restrictions:

(3 a.m. - 7 a.m.) $\quad -.2X_1 - .2X_6 - .2Y_1 + .8Y_5 - .2Y_6 \leqq 0$

(7 a.m. - 11 a.m.) $\quad -.2X_1 - .2X_2 - .2Y_1 - .2Y_2 + .8Y_6 \leqq 0$

(11 a.m. - 3 p.m.) $\quad -.2X_2 - .2X_3 + .8Y_1 - .2Y_2 - .2Y_3 \leqq 0$

(3 p.m. - 7 p.m.) $\quad -.2X_3 - .2X_4 + .8Y_2 - .2Y_3 - .2Y_4 \leqq 0$

(7 p.m. - 11 p.m.) $\quad -.2X_4 - .2X_5 + .8Y_3 - .2Y_4 - .2Y_5 \leqq 0$

(11 p.m. - 3 a.m.) $\quad -.2X_5 - .2X_6 + .8Y_4 - .2Y_5 - .2Y_6 \leqq 0$

all X_i and $Y_i \geqq 0$

6. We must decide how much of each mix to make <u>and</u> how to make it. This can be done by deciding how much of each basic candy type to use in making each mix.

Define: $b(m)$ = the number of pounds of basic candy type b, to use in making mix m, where:
b = C, N, J, M
m = R, D, S
(e.g., C(R) = the number of pounds of Cream centers used in Regular mix)

The objective is to maximize net revenue, which is the revenue from selling the mixes minus the cost of making the basic candy types. Note that selling prices are per <u>two</u> pounds, so they will be halved to give a per pound revenue.

maximize $\quad (2.00 - 1.00)C(R) + (2.25 - 1.00)C(D)$
$\quad + (2.50 - 1.00)C(S) + (2.00 - 1.25)N(R)$
$\quad + (2.25 - 1.25)N(D) + (2.50 - 1.25)N(S)$
$\quad + (2.00 - 1.40)J(R) + (2.25 - 1.40)J(D)$
$\quad + (2.50 - 1.40)J(S) + (2.00 - 1.70)M(R)$
$\quad + (2.25 - 1.70)M(D) + (2.50 - 1.70)M(S)$

maximize $\quad 1.00C(R) + 1.25C(D) + 1.50C(S) + 0.75N(R)$
$\quad + 1.00N(D) + 1.25N(S) + 0.60J(R) + 0.85J(D)$
$\quad + 1.10J(S) + 0.30M(R) + 0.55J(D) + 0.80M(S)$

subject to:

Basic candy type availability:

$\quad C(R) + C(D) + C(S) \leq 250$
$\quad N(R) + N(D) + N(S) \leq 250$
$\quad J(R) + J(D) + J(S) \leq 150$
$\quad M(R) + M(D) + M(S) \leq 75$

Blending constraints:

Regular mix:
$\quad .7C(R) - .3N(R) - .3J(R) - .3M(R) \leq 0 \quad$ (Cream)
$\quad -.3C(R) + .7N(R) - .3J(R) - .3M(R) \leq 0 \quad$ (Nut)
$\quad -.2C(R) - .2N(R) + .8J(R) - .2M(R) \geq 0 \quad$ (Jelly)
No limits on Mint.

Deluxe mix:
$\quad .8C(D) - .2N(D) - .2J(D) - .2M(D) \leq 0 \quad$ (Cream)
$\quad -.2C(D) + .8N(D) - .2J(D) - .2M(D) \leq 0 \quad$ (Nut)
$\quad -.1C(D) - .1N(D) + .9J(D) - .1M(D) \geq 0 \quad$ (Jelly)
$\quad -.1C(D) - .1N(D) - .1J(D) + .9M(D) \geq 0 \quad$ (Mint)

Supreme mix:
$\quad .9C(S) - .1N(S) - .1J(S) - .1M(S) \leq 0 \quad$ (Cream)
$\quad -.2C(S) + .8N(S) - .2J(S) - .2M(S) \leq 0 \quad$ (Nut)
$\quad - 1C(S) - .1N(S) + .9J(S) - .1M(S) \geq 0 \quad$ (Jelly)
$\quad -.2C(S) - .2N(S) - .2J(S) + .8M(S) \geq 0 \quad$ (Mint)

all $b(m) \geq 0$

7. The problem is to determine how much to produce each period on both regular and overtime.

   Define: $R(1) - R(6)$ = number of units produced each period on regular time

   $P(1) - P(6)$ = number of units produced each period on overtime

   $I(1) - I(6)$ = number of units in inventory at the <u>end</u> of each period

The objective is to minimize total cost, which is the sum of regular and overtime production costs plus inventory carrying cost.

minimize $10R(1) + 15P(1) + I(1) + 10R(2) + 15P(2) + I(2)$
$+ 10R(3) + 15P(3) + I(3) + 10P(4) + 15P(4) + I(4)$
$+ 10R(5) + 15P(5) + I(5) + 10R(6) + 15P(6) + I(6)$

subject to:

  Meet Demands:
$$R(1) + P(1) - I(1) = 2400 \quad (=2500 - 100)$$
$$R(2) + P(2) + I(1) - I(2) = 2200$$
$$R(3) + P(3) + I(2) - I(3) = 2700$$
$$R(4) + P(4) + I(3) - I(4) = 3000$$
$$R(5) + P(5) + I(4) - I(5) = 3200$$
$$R(6) + P(6) + I(5) - I(6) = 2400$$
  Inventory Limits:
$$I(1) \leq 300$$
$$I(2) \leq 300$$
$$I(3) \leq 300$$
$$I(4) \leq 300$$
$$I(5) \leq 300$$
$$I(6) = 150 \quad \text{(Ending Requirement)}$$

Regular Production Limits:	Overtime Production Limits:
$R(1) \leq 2700$	$P(1) \leq 540$
$R(2) \leq 2700$	$P(2) \leq 540$
$R(3) \leq 2700$	$P(3) \leq 540$
$R(4) \leq 2700$	$P(4) \leq 540$
$R(5) \leq 2700$	$P(5) \leq 540$
$R(6) \leq 2700$	$P(6) \leq 540$

  All $R(i)$, $P(i)$, and $I(i) \geq 0$

8. The problem is to determine how much to produce at each brewery and send to each distribution center.

Define: $b(d)$ = barrels to send from brewery b to distribution center d

    where b = H,A,S
           d = E,F,A

The total brewery-distribution center cost is the sum of the production cost and the shipping cost.

21

```
minimize    5.10H(E) + 4.20H(F) + 4.50H(A)
          + 4.20A(E) + 4.10A(F) + 3.95A(A)
          + 4.80S(E) + 4.10S(F) + 4.00S(A)

subject to:

    Satisfy All Demands:
      H(E) + A(E) + S(E) = 900     (El Paso)
      H(F) + A(F) + S(F) = 600     (Fort Worth)
      H(A) + A(A) + S(A) = 400     (Abilene)

    Capacity Limits:
      H(E) + H(F) + H(A) ≤ 500     (Houston)
      A(E) + A(F) + A(A) ≤ 600     (Amarillo)
      S(E) + S(F) + S(A) ≤ 1000    (San Antonio)

    all b(d) ≥ 0
```

Chapter Test

1. c	3. b	5. d	7. d	9. a
2. d	4. b	6. a	8. b	10. c

CHAPTER THREE

SOLVING LP PROBLEMS: GRAPHICAL METHOD

MAIN POINTS

1. The graphical method for solving LP problems is not applicable to realistic problems since it is limited to no more than three variables. Its value is instructional, providing an intuitive understanding of the concepts in the simplex method (the subject of Chapter 4) and sensitivity analysis. The discussion here is limited to two-variable problems.

2. The graphical method for solving LP problems is a two-phase process: (1) plot the problem's constraints to find the region of feasible solutions; (2) search this region to find the optimal solution.

3. The first step is to establish a coordinate grid system to display the values of the variables, identifying an axis for each decision variable. In most cases the variables are required to be nonnegative so the graph is confined to the positive quadrant.

4. Next is to determine which section of the positive quadrant is feasible by graphing the constraints. The determination of which points satisfy an inequality constraint begins with graphing the equation at its boundary. If the constraint involves a single variable, the boundary line will be horizontal or vertical, crossing the appropriate axis at the value which that variable must be $\leq$ or $\geq$. If the constraint involves both variables, the boundary line is graphed by determining two points on the line and connecting them. In most cases these two points will be where the constraint boundary line crosses the two axes, setting, in turn, each variable equal to zero and solving for the axis-crossing value of the other. If the constraint's variable coefficients are of opposite sign the process is more difficult but it still involves finding two points on the line and connecting them. Once the boundary line is graphed the inequality portion (if there is one) can be established by substituting any pair of coordinate values (usually the origin) into the inequality to see if it is satisfied.

5. When all constraints have been graphed the feasible region is found by identifying the set of points that satisfy all constraints, the overlap of the individual constraint's feasible sets. It is possible that there is no overlap, in which case there is no answer to the problem.

6. Once the feasible region has been found, the search for the optimal solution begins. An important result is the Extreme Point Theorem which says that if there is an optimal solution then one of them will be at an extreme point or corner of the feasible set. Thus we need only check the corners to find an optimum.

7. It is possible to solve for the coordinates of all extreme points and substitute them into the objective function to identify the best. This

23

brute force method will be time consuming, however, if there are many corners.

8. A more efficient procedure involves graphing the objective function. By setting the objective function equal to a reasonable value, a member of the objective line family is found. Other values give other members, all of which are parallel. The idea is to find the "best" member of that family, the one corresponding to the largest value for a maximization problem or to the smallest value for a minimization problem, that still touches the feasible region. This can generally be done by putting a ruler or other straight-edge on the representative line graphed and moving it, parallel to that line, in the direction of improvement.

9. Once an optimal extreme point has been identified, the coordinates can be found by solving simultaneously the two equations that define the corner. The optimal value for the objective function is then found by substituting those coordinates into the objective function expression.

10. Summary of process:
    a. Plot each constraint as an equation.
    b. Determine each constraint's feasible region and the intersection of them all.
    c. Plot the objective function for a specific value.
    d. Move the objective function in the direction of improvement until you reach the best extreme point.
    e. Find the coordinates of that extreme point by solving simultaneously the two boundary line equations that define that point.

11. Solving maximization and minimization problems are essentially the same. The first difference is that the feasible region for a maximization problem is usually near the origin while that for a minimization problem generally extends away from the origin, past a constraint line boundary. The second difference relates to the objective function. In most (but not all), minimization problems, we are looking for the objective function line closest to the origin whereas most maximization problems involve moving the objective function line away from the origin.

12. A binding constraint is one that is met as an equality at the optimal solution. Graphically, its equation line passes through the optimal solution point. If a constraint is not binding it has slack. This concept is important for the simplex solution procedure in Chapter 4.

13. In solving some LP problems, special cases will be encountered: alternative optima, unbounded solutions, and no feasible solution.

14. If the objective function line is parallel to one of the boundary lines that defines an optimal extreme point, then there will be a second optimal extreme point, also on that same boundary line. All points on the boundary line segment connecting those two points are also optimal.

15. It is possible that the graph of the problem shows that the objective function can be improved without limit. If this happens, it indicates the problem was improperly modeled since realistic problems do not have unlimited value.

16. If the feasible sets for individual constraints do not intersect, there is no feasible solution. This may indicate improper modeling but may also mean that the decision maker is trying to accomplish something that cannot be done.

KEY TERMS

Match each term with the appropriate definition below.

Terms

__C__ 1. alternate optima   __A__ 4. feasible region

__B__ 2. binding constraint   __D__ 5. graphical method

__F__ 3. extreme point   __E__ 6. optimal solution

Definitions

A. The set of points which satisfy all constraints.

B. A constraint that is met as an equality at the optimal solution.

C. The situation in which there is more than one solution with the same "best" value.

D. A procedure that can be used for solving LP problems with a maximum of three variables.

E. The feasible point with the best solution value.

F. A feasible point at the intersection of constraint boundary lines.

SOLVED PROBLEM

Problem 2 from the review exercises of Chapter 2 can be modeled as:

$$
\begin{aligned}
\text{minimize} \quad & .40X + .45Y \\
\text{subject to} \quad & 1X + 2Y \geq 50 \quad \text{(A)} \\
& 1.5X + 1Y \geq 45 \quad \text{(B)} \\
& 2X + 2Y \geq 80 \quad \text{(C)} \\
& X, Y \geq 0
\end{aligned}
$$

Solve this problem graphically and determine which constraints are binding and how much slack exists in each constraint.

Solution

To plot the three inequalities, we must first determine the X- and Y-axis intercepts. Setting $Y = 0$, we find that the X intercept of constraint A is 50; likewise, setting $X = 0$ yields $Y = 25$. Thus constraint A passes through points (50,0) and (0,25). Since constraint A is a greater-than-or-equal constraint, we must also determine which half of the plane satisfies the constraint. Substituting the origin (0,0) in constraint A ($0+0 \not\geq 50$) does not

25

satisfy the constraint, thus we shade the side of constraint A away from the origin. In a similar manner, we determine that the intercepts for constraints B and C are (30,0), (40,0) and (40,0), (0,40), respectively. Both of these constraints have graphs whose regions shade away from the origin. The graph below shows the resulting feasible region.

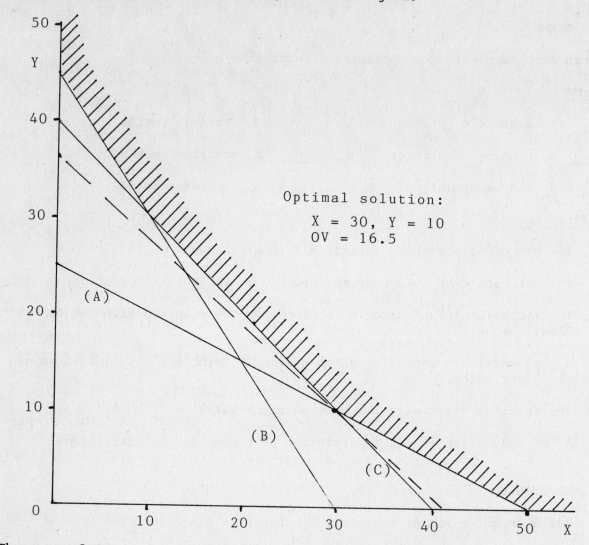

There are four extreme points that are candidates for the optimal solution. We can zero in on the optimal point by plotting the objective function. Graphing the objective function for a particular value such as:

$$.40X + .45Y = 15$$

yields an isocost line (the dashed line) that pinpoints the intersection of constraints A and C as the optimal extreme point. Solving the equality forms of A and C simultaneously yields:

$$1X + 2Y = 50$$
$$2X + 2Y = 80$$

or

$$-X - 2Y = -50$$
$$\underline{2X + 2Y = 80}$$
$$X = 30$$

Substituting in the first equation yields:

$$30 + 2Y = 50 \qquad \text{or} \qquad Y = 20/2 = 10$$

26

Thus, the optimal solution is the point (30,10) with an objective function value of

$$.40(30) + .45(10) = 16.5$$

Constraints A and C are binding since they pass through the optimal point; they have zero slack. The slack for constraint B can be calculated as

$$1.5(30) + 1(10) - 45 = 55 - 45 = 10$$

REVIEW EXERCISES

1. Consider the LP problem:

    maximize   6X + 10Y
    subject to 3X + 6Y ≤ 30
                8X + 6Y ≤ 48
                 X, Y ≥ 0

    a. Find all the extreme points and evaluate the objective function at each

    b. Use the "move the objective function line" approach to confirm your choice of optimum.

    c. Suppose the objective function changed to 4X + 10Y. Would this change the optimal solution?

2. Solve Problem 1 from the Review Exercises of Chapter 2.

3. Mabel's Machine Shop has an order to produce ten identical gears. There are two processes by which they might be produced. The first process requires 5 hours on Machine 1 and 3 hours on Machine 2. The second process requires 4 hours on Machine 1 and 6 hours on Machine 2. There are 45 hours available on Machine 1 and 54 hours available on Machine 2. The first process will cost $10 to produce a gear and the second process will cost $12. Determine how Mabel should produce the required gears at minimum cost.

4. For each of the following problems indicate whether the problem has a unique optimal solution, multiple optimal solutions, no feasible solution, or an unbounded solution.

    a. maximize   5X + 2Y
       subject to: X + 2Y ≤ 4
                      3X + 5Y ≥ 15
                       X, Y ≥ 0

    b. maximize   3X + 2Y
       subject to: X   ≤ 6
                       X - Y ≤ 2
                       X, Y ≥ 0

    c. maximize   2X + 3Y
       subject to: 5X + 3Y ≥ 15
                      4X + 6Y ≥ 24
                       X, Y ≥ 0

CHAPTER TEST

1. The graphical solution procedure is:
   a. useful for obtaining a quick solution to most LP problems.
   b. helpful for understanding the concepts of LP solution.
   c. both of the above.
   d. neither of the above.

2. If one coefficient in the objective function is changed, it will:
   a. change the slope of the objective function line.
   b. always change the optimum solution.
   c. always change the value of the objective function.
   d. all of the above.

3. If the right-hand side of a less-than-or-equal-to constraint is reduced in a maximization problem it will:
   a. reduce the value of the objective function.
   b. increase the value of the objective function.
   c. have no effect on the value of the objective function.
   d. It is impossible to tell without more information about the problem.

4. Assuming that one exists, an optimal solution to a LP problem:
   a. may occur at a point strictly interior to the feasible set.
   b. is always unique.
   c. can be found at an extreme point of the feasible set.
   d. always occurs at the intersection of resource or requirement constraints.

5. The boundary lines of the feasible set are straight line segments because:
   a. two points define a straight line.
   b. the constraints are linear expressions.
   c. the objective function is a linear expression.
   d. the variables must be nonnegative.

6. Suppose a LP problem has been solved graphically to find an optimal solution. A new constraint is added. The result is:
   a. if the previously optimal solution is still feasible, it is still optimal.
   b. there may no longer be a feasible solution.
   c. another extreme point may become optimal.
   d. all of the above.

7. Which of the following statements is <u>true</u>?
   a. Any LP problem can be solved graphically.
   b. The feasible region for the LP problem is the overlap of the feasible regions for its constraints.
   c. The optimal solution always occurs at a single point.
   d. All are true.

8. If the objective function is set equal to an arbitrarily chosen value and graphed:
   a. any point on the line is a feasible solution.
   b. the optimal solution will occur where it crosses a constraint line.
   c. the line will be parallel to the line for any other value.
   d. all of the above.

28

9. Multiple optimal solutions:
    a. occur when the number of constraints exceeds the number of variables.
    b. occur when the objective function is parallel to a binding constraint.
    c. are limited to exactly two in number.
    d. do not occur in minimization problems.

10. In an LP problem with nonnegativity and two constraints
        3X + 4Y ≤ 12
        6X + 2Y ≤ 12
    the extreme points of the feasible set are:
    a. (0,0), (4,0), (4/3,2), (0,3)
    b. (0,0), (2,0), (4/3,2), (0,6)
    c. (0,0), (2,0), (4/3,2), (0,3)
    d. (0,0), (4,0), (4/3,2), (0,6)
    The numbers in the pair are (X,Y).

ANSWER KEY

Key Terms

1. C   3. F   5. D
2. B   4. A   6. E

Review Exercises

1.

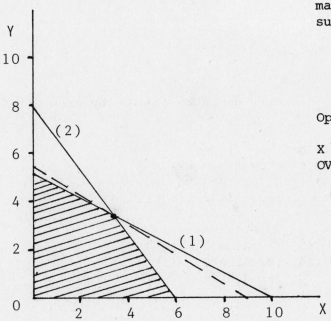

maximize   6X + 10Y
subject to   3X + 6Y ≤ 30   (1)
               8X + 6Y ≤ 48   (2)
               X, Y ≥ 0

Optimal solution

X = 3.6,   Y = 3.2
OV = 53.6

2. Refer to page 17 for the definition of the decision variables.

maximize   10A + 12B
subject to   2A + 6B $\leq$ 30   (T)
               5A + 4B $\leq$ 40   (P)
               6A + 4B $\leq$ 60   (M)
               A, B $\geqq$ 0

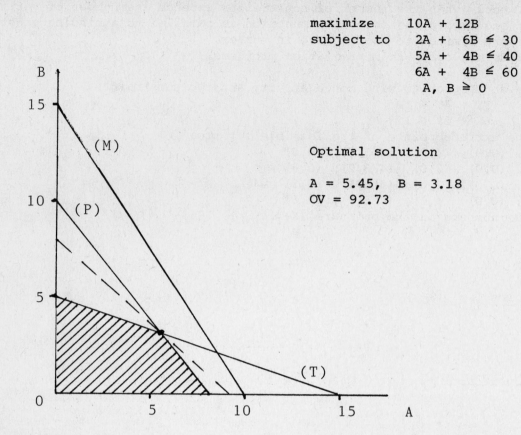

Optimal solution

A = 5.45, B = 3.18
OV = 92.73

3. The problem is to determine how many gears to produce by each of the two processes.

Define: X = number of gears made by Process 1
         Y = number of gears made by Process 2

The objective is to minimize the cost of production.

minimize   10X + 12Y
subject to   5X + 3Y $\leq$ 45   Machine 1   (1)
              4X + 6Y $\leq$ 54   Machine 2   (2)
               X +   Y = 10   Production (P)
               X, Y $\geqq$ 0

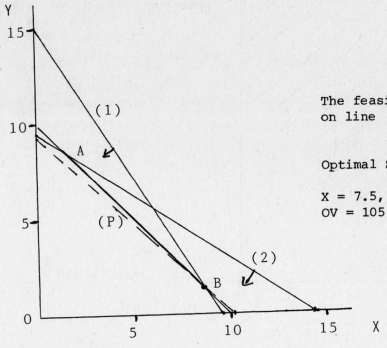

The feasible set is the points
on line (P) between A and B.

Optimal Solution: Corner B

X = 7.5,   Y = 2.5
OV = 105

4. a.

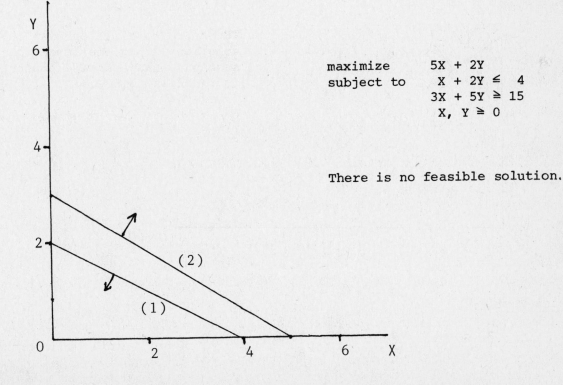

maximize   5X + 2Y
subject to   X + 2Y ≤ 4
              3X + 5Y ≥ 15
               X, Y ≥ 0

There is no feasible solution.

31

b.

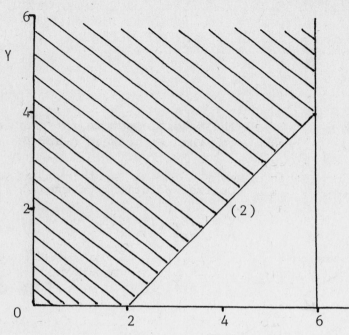

maximize   3X + 2Y
subject to   X   ≦ 6   (1)
               X – Y ≦ 2   (2)
               X, Y ≧ 0

The solution is unbounded.

c.

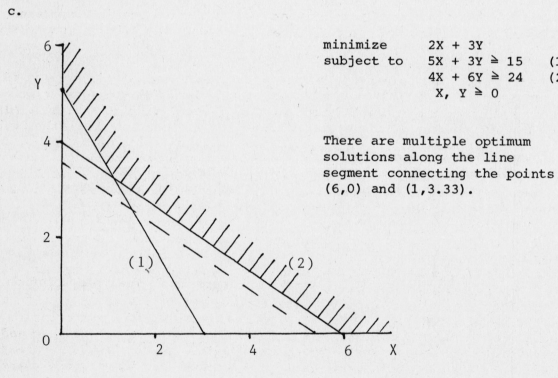

minimize   2X + 3Y
subject to   5X + 3Y ≧ 15   (1)
               4X + 6Y ≧ 24   (2)
               X, Y ≧ 0

There are multiple optimum
solutions along the line
segment connecting the points
(6,0) and (1,3.33).

Chapter Test

1. b   3. d   5. b   7. b   9. b
2. a   4. c   6. d   8. c   10. c

CHAPTER FOUR

SOLVING LP PROBLEMS: SIMPLEX METHOD

MAIN POINTS

1. Since the graphical solution procedure for LP problems is limited to problems with two or three variables, an easily computerized systematic procedure capable of handling realistic problems with hundreds or thousands of variables is needed. The simplex method, developed by George Dantzig in 1947, is one such method.

2. The simplex method is a systematic algebraic procedure, an algorithm, that examines the extreme points of the feasible set of an LP problem in a sequence such that each solution is at least as good as the one before it. The procedure guarantees that, assuming one exists, an optimal solution will be found in a finite number of steps or iterations. It is based on the Gaussian elimination procedure for solving systems of simultaneous linear equations.

3. After making sure that the right-hand sides of all constraints are nonnegative, the simplex method requires the converting of each constraint into an equation, transforming the problem to <u>standard form</u>. A <u>slack</u> variable is added to the left side of each ≤ constraint to make it an equation. If the constraint represents a resource limit, the slack is the amount of that resource unused in a solution. If the constraint is of the ≥ type, the slack is subtracted from the left side. This is also known as a surplus variable and represents the amount by which the lower bound is exceeded. For any constraint without an added slack (i.e., for ≥ constraints and equalities), an <u>artificial variable</u> is added. An artificial variable violates the original constraint and thus is not allowed to appear in the final solution. It is only included to facilitate finding a feasible solution for the simplex method to work from.

4. Once the slack and artificial variables have been added to create the equations in standard form, the total number of variables exceeds the number of constraints. If the number of equations is m, we can set all but m of the variables equal to zero and solve for the values of the m remaining variables. If such a solution exists it is called <u>basic</u>. If the values solved for in a basic solution also satisfy all the constraints, including nonnegativity, it is a <u>basic feasible solution</u> and corresponds to an extreme point of the feasible set for the LP. The simplex method works with basic feasible solutions, moving from one extreme point to an adjacent one with at least as good a value for the objective function.

5. The simplex procedure consists of four steps:
1. Determine an initial feasible (or, if it uses any artificial variables, pseudofeasible) basic solution.
2. Determine whether the solution can be improved by replacing some basic variable by a currently nonbasic variable. If not, stop. If yes, select the <u>entering variable</u>.

3. Determine the <u>leaving variable</u> as that basic variable that will reach zero first as the entering variable is increased.

4. Update the coefficients of the equation set by <u>pivoting</u>. Return to step 2.

One complete repetition of steps 2 through 4 is called an <u>iteration</u>. For large problems thousands of iterations may be required.

6. The simplex procedure is carried out with a standard numerical layout called a <u>simplex tableau</u>, which is, initially, a matrix of the coefficients of the variables in the standard form of the LP problem supplemented with additional rows, to show the objective function coefficients and the indicator values needed for step 2 of the procedure, and columns to indicate which variables are basic, their objective function coefficients, and their values in the solution. As the iterations of the procedure are carried out, the numbers in the tableau are revised with the row operations of Gaussian elimination to reflect the new basic solution, and the name of the entering variable replaces the name of the leaving variable in the basic variable name column.

7. The initial solution consists of the "added" dummy variables. If the constraint was originally less-than-or-equal-to, this is slack. If the constraint was originally an equation or greater-than-or-equal-to, it is an artificial variable. All other variables—decision variables and subtracted slacks—are nonbasic and equal to zero.

8. The simplex tableau column for a nonbasic variable gives the <u>substitution coefficients</u> between the nonbasic variable of the column and the basic variables defined by the rows. A positive substitution coefficient means that as the incoming (nonbasic) variable enters the solution, the basic variable is reduced. If the substitution coefficient is negative, the basic variable would increase with the increase in the incoming variable.

9. The next-to-bottom row of the tableau—the Z_j row—shows for each variable what it would cost, in terms of the change in value of the present basic variables and their contribution to the objective function, to bring that variable into the solution. The Z_j values are found by multiplying the column of substitution coefficients times the objective function coefficients of the basic variables and summing.

10. The bottom row of the tableau—the $C_j - Z_j$ row—are the optimality or improvement indicators, also known as <u>reduced costs</u> or opportunity costs. If the objective function coefficient, C_j, exceeds the cost of introducing the nonbasic variable, Z_j, then the value of the objective function may be increased by bringing that nonbasic variable into the solution. If $C_j - Z_j$ is negative for a nonbasic variable, the objective function may be reduced. Thus, if the problem is one of maximization, the procedure continues as long as there is any positive $C_j - Z_j$ value. If the objective function is to be minimized, it continues as long as any negative $C_j - Z_j$ exists.

11. The <u>incoming variable</u> is the nonbasic variable with the most positive (for maximization) or most negative (for minimization) $C_j - Z_j$ value. The column for that variable is the <u>pivot column</u>.

12. The <u>outgoing variable</u> is the basic variable that will reach zero first as the incoming variable is increased. It is identified by taking the

34

ratios of the solution values to the substitution coefficients for positive coefficients only. The <u>smallest</u> ratio shows which variable will leave the basis. The outgoing variable row is the <u>pivot row</u> and its intersection with the pivot column determines the <u>pivot element</u> of the tableau.

13. Updating the tableau to reflect the introduction of the incoming variable and dropping the outgoing variable is a two step process.
<u>Step 1</u>: The pivot row is updated to represent the new basic variable by multiplying the coefficients in that row by the reciprocal of the pivot element. The new basic variable name and objective function coefficient replace the leaving variable's name and coefficient on the left side of the tableau.
<u>Step 2</u>: The remaining basic-variable rows and the C_j-Z_j row are updated with a Gaussian elimination row operation. The updated pivot row is multiplied by row i's coefficient in the pivot column and subtracted from the old row i to give an updated row i (for all rows except the pivot row).

14. The iterations continue as long as the C_j-Z_j row indicators show that improvement of the objective function is possible.

15. There are two methods for handling the elimination of artificial variables from the basis. The authors present the "<u>Big M</u>" method in which the artificial variables are incorporated into the objective function with a very high cost--a large positive value (a big M if doing the problem by hand) for a minimization problem or a large negative value for a maximization problem. The best way to improve the value of the objective function is to eliminate the artificial variables from the solution.

16. The alternative is the <u>phase I/phase II</u> method. In phase I, the objective function to be minimized is the sum of the artificial variables. If this sum can be reduced to zero by eliminating the artificial variables, the objective function is replaced (phase II) by the real objective function, the Z_j and C_j-Z_j rows are recomputed, and the algorithm continues using the new objective function and optimality indicators.

17. The special cases of LP can be easily identified from the simplex tableau.
a. An <u>unbounded</u> solution is indicated if the incoming variable's column consists of only nonpositive substitution coefficients.
b. If the artificial variables cannot be eliminated from the basis, there is <u>no feasible</u> solution.
c. If, in the optimal tableau, there is a nonbasic variable with a C_j-Z_j value of zero, there is an <u>alternate optimum</u> solution.
d. If two variables tie for the minimum ratio when determining the leaving variable, <u>degeneracy</u> exists. The variable in the higher row of the tableau is replaced in the basis. The other is retained as basic with value zero.

18. LP software packages are available from most computer manufacturers for their equipment as well as from independent software distributors. In addition, LP packages are available through many time-sharing services. For large-scale problems the solution code is often supplemented by a preprocessor or matrix generator to put the correct coefficient values in the right places and by a report generator to interpret the solution.

KEY TERMS

Match each term with the appropriate definition below.

Terms

J 1. artificial variable

F 2. basic feasible solution

P 3. basic solution

H 4. basic variable

S 5. Big M method

A 6. degeneracy

L 7. elementary row operations

V 8. entering variable

T 9. iteration

N 10. leaving variable

B 11. nonbasic variable

G 12. phase I/phase II approach

O 13. optimality criterion

U 14. pivot column

E 15. pivot element

Q 16. pivoting

M 17. pivot row

C 18. reduced cost

K 19. simplex tableau

I 20. slack variable

R 21. standard form

D 22. substitution coefficient

Definitions

A. The condition in which a basic variable equals zero.

B. A variable not included in the solution.

C. The opportunity cost of introducing a nonbasic variable into the solution.

D. Shows the effect on a basic variable of introducing a nonbasic variable into the solution.

E. The substitution coefficient at the intersection of the incoming variable's column and the leaving variable's row.

F. A basic solution that satisfies all constraints.

G. A method for eliminating artificial variables that starts with minimizing the sum of the artificial variables.

H. A variable included in the solution set.

I. Shows the amount of a resource that is left over.

J. Included in equality and $\geq$ constraints to provide an initial solution.

K. A matrix displaying the relevant coefficients of the equations of an LP.

L. The operations used in updating the coefficients of the simplex tableau to reflect a new basis.

M. The simplex tableau row of the leaving variable.

N. The basic variable that first reaches zero as a new variable enters the solution.

O. All C_j-Z_j values are $\leq$ zero for a maximization problem ($\geq$ zero for a minimization problem).

P. An LP solution found by setting all but m variables equal to zero and solving for the rest (where m is the number of structural constraints).

Q. Using elementary row operations to update the coefficients of the simplex tableau.

R. The result of converting all LP constraints to equations with slack and artificial variables.

S. A method for eliminating artificial variables by including them in the objective function with large coefficients.

T. One complete execution of the steps of the simplex method.

U. The simplex tableau column of the incoming variable.

V. The nonbasic variable with the most positive (for a maximization) or negative (for a minimization) C_j-Z_j value.

SOLVED PROBLEM

Calculate the simplex solution for Review Exercise 1 of Chapter 2. Verify the graphical solution from Review Exercise 2 of Chapter 3.

Solution

The model can be restated as:

$$\begin{aligned}
\text{maximize} \quad & 10A + 12B \\
\text{subject to:} \quad & 2A + 6B \leq 30 \\
& 5A + 4B \leq 40 \\
& 6A + 4B \leq 60 \\
& A, B \geq 0
\end{aligned}$$

To use the simplex method, it is necessary to convert the model to standard form. Since all constraints are =, we add one slack variable to each of the constraints.

$$\begin{aligned}
\text{maximize} \quad & 10A + 12B + 0S1 + 0S2 + 0S3 \\
\text{subject to:} \quad & 2A + 6B + S1 \qquad\qquad = 30 \\
& 5A + 4B \qquad + S2 \qquad = 40 \\
& 6A + 4B \qquad\qquad + S3 = 60
\end{aligned}$$

The initial simplex tableau is:

C_B	C_j Basic Variables	10 A	12 B	0 S1	0 S2	0 S3	Solution	Ratio
0	S1	2	⑥	1	0	0	30	5
0	S2	5	4	0	1	0	40	10
0	S3	6	4	0	0	1	60	15
	Z_j	0	0	0	0	0	0	
	C_j-Z_j	10	12	0	0	0		

The variable with the most positive C_j-Z_j value in this maximization problem is B with a "relative cost" of 12. Calculating the ratios between the B column and the solution column yields 5 as the minimum ratio. Thus, variable B will enter the solution and variable S1 in row 1 (where the minimum ratio occurred) will leave the solution. The circled number 6 is the pivot element and it occurs at the intersection of the column of the entering variable and the row of the leaving variable.

To determine the solution value of variable B and update the simplex tableau, we use elementary row operations. First, we convert the pivot element to a one by dividing row 1 by the pivot element 6. This yields the updated pivot row

$$2/6 \quad 1 \quad 1/6 \quad 0 \quad 0 \quad 5$$

To convert the column under basic variable B to the unit vector $\begin{pmatrix}1\\0\\0\end{pmatrix}$, we must now eliminate the 4 in column 2 of rows 2 and 3. To eliminate the 4 in row 2, we multiply the updated pivot row by 4 and subtract it from row 2. We obtain:

$$
\begin{array}{cccccc}
5 & 4 & 0 & 1 & 0 & 40 \\
- \quad 4(2/6) & 4(1) & 4(1/6) & 4(0) & 4(0) & 4(5) \\
\hline
3.667 & 0 & -0.667 & 1 & 0 & 20
\end{array}
$$

Repeating the same procedure for row 3 yields:

$$
\begin{array}{cccccc}
6 & 4 & 0 & 0 & 1 & 60 \\
- \quad 4(2/6) & 4(1) & 4(1/6) & 4(0) & 4(0) & 4(5) \\
\hline
4.667 & 0 & -0.667 & 0 & 1 & 40
\end{array}
$$

This yields the updated tableau:

C_B	C_j Basic Variables	10 A	12 B	0 S1	0 S2	0 S3	Solution	Ratio
12	B	0.333	1	.167	0	0	5	15
0	S2	③.667	0	-.667	1	0	20	5.455
0	S3	4.667	0	-.667	0	1	40	8.571
	Z_j	4	12	2	0	0	60	
	C_j-Z_j	6	0	-2	0	0		

Notice that variable A is the only variable with a $C_j - Z_j \geq 0$, thus A is the next entering variable. The minimum ratio test yields 5.455 as the minimum ratio in row 2. Thus, S2 is the leaving variable and 3.667 becomes the pivot element. Updating the tableau using elementary row operations yields the next tableau.

C_B	Basic Variables	A	B	S1	S2	S3	Solution
	C_j	10	12	0	0	0	
12	B	0	1	.227	-.091	0	3.182
10	A	1	0	-.182	.273	0	5.455
0	S3	0	0	.182	-1.273	1	14.545
	Z_j	10	12	.909	1.636	0	92.727
	$C_j - Z_j$	0	0	-.909	-1.636	0	

Note that no variable has a $C_j - Z_j > 0$ and all solution values are ≥ 0. Thus, the solution is optimal.

A = 5.455, B = 3.182, S3 = 14.545, Objective Function = 92.727

REVIEW EXERCISES

1. Solve Problem 2 from the Review Exercises of Chapter 2 using the simplex method. Verify your result from Review Exercise 3 of Chapter 3.

2. Use the simplex method to solve the problems in Review Exercise 4 from Chapter 3 to confirm your conclusions.

3. Use the simplex method to solve:

maximize $\quad 11X_1 + 7X_2 + X_3$

subject to: $\quad 5X_1 + 3X_2 + 2X_3 \leq 1000$

$\quad\quad\quad\quad 4X_1 + 3X_2 + 2X_3 \leq 800$

$\quad\quad\quad\quad X_1 + 2X_2 + 2X_3 \leq 400$

$\quad\quad\quad\quad X_1, X_2, X_3 \geq 0$

4. Use the simplex method to solve:

maximize $\quad 22X_1 + 34X_2 + 23X_3 + 33X_4$

subject to: $\quad 4X_1 + 3X_2 \leq 48$

$\quad\quad\quad\quad 5X_3 + 5X_4 \leq 40$

$\quad\quad\quad\quad X_1 + X_3 \geq 13$

$\quad\quad\quad\quad X_2 + X_4 \geq 7$

$\quad\quad\quad\quad X_1, X_2, X_3, X_4 \geq 0$

1. To convert a $\leq$ inequality with a positive right-hand side for transformation to standard form, we:
    a. change the signs of the coefficients and the direction of the inequality.
    b. add a slack variable.
    c. subtract a slack variable and add an artificial variable.
    d. add an artificial variable only.

2. To convert a $\geq$ inequality with a positive right-hand side for transformation to standard form, we:
    a. change the signs of the coefficients and the direction of the inequality.
    b. add a slack variable.
    c. subtract a slack variable and add an artificial variable.
    d. add an artificial variable only.

3. To convert an equation with a positive right-hand side for transformation to standard form we:
    a. change the signs of the coefficients and the direction of the equality.
    b. add a slack variable.
    c. subtract a slack variable and add an artificial variable.
    d. add an artificial variable only.

4. In a maximization problem optimality is reached when:
    a. all Z_j values are positive.
    b. all substitution coefficients are nonnegative.
    c. all reduced costs are nonnegative.
    d. all reduced costs are nonpositive.

5. If in the final simplex tableau we have a reduced cost that indicates that improvement is possible and its substitution coefficient column is all nonpositive, we have:
    a. no feasible solution.
    b. an unbounded solution.
    c. an alternate optimum solution.
    d. one optimal solution.

6. If in the final simplex tableau, we have a zero reduced cost for a non-basic variable, then we have:
    a. no feasible solution.
    b. an unbounded solution.
    c. an alternate optimum solution.
    d. one optimal solution.

7. If in the final simplex tableau, one of the basic variables is an artificial variable with a positive value, we have:
    a. no feasible solution.
    b. an unbounded solution.
    c. an alternate optimum solution.
    d. one optimal solution.

8. The incoming variable in a maximization problem is identified as the variable for which:
   a. $C_j = Z_j$.
   b. $C_j - Z_j$ is most positive.
   c. $C_j - Z_j$ is most negative.
   d. the solution value - substitution coefficient ratio is largest.

9. The leaving variable is identified as the basic variable for which:
   a. the solution value to positive substitution coefficient ratio is largest.
   b. the solution value to positive substitution coefficient ratio is smallest.
   c. the solution value is smallest.
   d. the objective function coefficient value is smallest.

10. Multiplying an artificial variable by a large cost and incorporating it into the objective function:
    a. is the Big M method.
    b. is the phase I/phase II method.
    c. guarantees that the artificial variable will be eliminated from the solution.
    d. both (a) and (c).

ANSWER KEY

Terms

1. J	5. S	9. T	13. O	17. M	21. R
2. F	6. A	10. N	14. U	18. C	22. D
3. P	7. L	11. B	15. E	19. K	
4. H	8. V	12. G	16. Q	20. I	

Review Exercises

1. Refer to page 25 for the model and solution.

$$
\begin{array}{ll}
\text{minimize} & .40X + .45Y \\
\text{subject to:} & 1X + 2Y \geq 50 \\
& 1.5X + 1Y \geq 45 \\
& 2X + 2Y \geq 80 \\
& X, Y \geq 0
\end{array}
$$

Converted to standard form, it becomes:

$$
\begin{array}{llll}
\text{minimize} & .40X + .45Y & + MA1 + MA2 + MA3 \\
\text{subject to:} & 1X + 2Y - S1 & + A1 & = 50 \\
& 1.5X + 1Y \quad - S2 & + A2 & = 45 \\
& 2X + 2Y \quad\quad - S3 & + A3 & = 80
\end{array}
$$

The initial simplex tableau is:

C_j		.40	.45	0	0	0	M	M	M		
C_B	Basic Variables	X	Y	S1	S2	S3	A1	A2	A3	Solution	Ratio
M	A1	1	②	-1	0	0	1	0	0	50	25
M	A2	1.5	1	0	-1	0	0	1	0	45	45
M	A3	2	2	0	0	-1	0	0	1	80	40
	Z_j	4.5M	5M	-M	-M	-M	M	M	M	175M	
	$C_j - Z_j$	.40-4.5M	.45-5M	M	M	M	0	0	0		

Y is the entering variable; A1 is the leaving variable.

C_j		.40	.45	0	0	0	M	M	M		
C_B	Basic Variables	X	Y	S1	S2	S3	A1	A2	A3	Solution	Ratio
.45	Y	.5	1	-.5	0	0	.5	0	0	25	25
M	A2	①	0	.5	-1	0	-.5	1	0	20	20
M	A3	1	0	1	0	-1	-1	0	1	30	30
	Z_j	.225+2M	.45	1.5M-.225	-M	M	.225-1.5M	M	M	50M+11.25	
	$C_j - Z_j$	.175-2M	0	.225-1.5M	M	M	2.5M-.225	0	0		

X is the entering variable; A2 is the leaving variable.

C_j		.40	.45	0	0	0	M	M	M		
C_B	Basic Variables	X	Y	S1	S2	S3	A1	A2	A3	Sol.	Ratio
.45	Y	0	1	-.75	.5	0	.75	-.5	0	15	30
.40	X	1	0	.50	-1	0	-.50	1	0	20	-
M	A3	0	0	.50	①	-1	-.50	-1	1	10	10
	Z_j	.4	.45	.5M-.1375	M-.175	-M	-.5M+.1375	-M+.175	M	10M+14.75	
	$C_j - Z_j$	0	0	.1375-.5M	.175-M	M	1.5M-.1375	2M-.175	0		

S2 is the entering variable; A3 is the leaving variable.

C_j		.40	.45	0	0	0	M	M	M	
C_B	Basic Variables	X	Y	S1	S2	S3	A1	A2	A3	Solution
.45	Y	0	1	-1	0	.5	1	0	-.5	10
.40	X	1	0	1	0	-1	-1	0	1	30
0	S2	0	0	.5	1	-1	-.5	-1	1	10
	Z_j	.4	.45	-.05	0	-.175	.05	0	.175	16.5
	$C_j - Z_j$	0	0	.05	0	.175	M-.05	M	M-.175	

The solution is optimal.
X = 30, Y = 10, S2 = 10, Objective Function = 16.5

2.
a. Refer to page 31 for the model and analysis.

maximize $5X + 2Y$
subject to: $X + 2Y \le 4$
           $3X + 5Y \ge 15$
           $X, Y \ge 0$

Converted to standard form, it becomes:

maximize $5X + 2Y$ $- MA2$
subject to: $X + 2Y + S1$ $= 4$
           $3X + 5Y$ $- S2 + A2 = 15$
           $X, Y, S1, S2, A2 \ge 0$

The initial simplex tableau is:

C_B	C_j	5	2	0	0	-M		
	Basic Variables	X	Y	S1	S2	A2	Solution	Ratio
0	S1	1	②	1	0	0	4	2
-M	A2	3	5	0	-1	1	15	3
	Z_j	-3M	-5M	0	M	-M	-15M	
	$C_j - Z_j$	5+3M	2+5M	0	-M	M		

Y is the entering variable; S1 is the leaving variable.

C_B	C_j	5	2	0	0	-M		
	Basic Variables	X	Y	S1	S2	A2	Solution	Ratio
2	Y	⑤	1	.5	0	0	2	4
-M	A2	.5	0	-2.5	-1	1	5	10
	Z_j	1-.5M	2	1+2.5M	M	-M	4-5M	
	$C_j - Z_j$	4+.5M	0	-1-2.5M	-M	0		

X is the entering variable; Y is the leaving variable.

C_B	C_j	5	2	0	0	-M	
	Basic Variables	X	Y	S1	S2	A2	Solution
5	X	1	2	1	0	0	4
-M	A2	0	-1	-3	-1	1	3
	Z_j	5	10+M	5+3M	M	-M	20-3M
	$C_j - Z_j$	0	-8-M	-5-3M	-M	0	

All $C_j - Z_j$ are ≤ 0, but an artificial variable is still in the solution, so there is <u>no feasible solution</u>.

43

b. Refer to page 32 for the model and analysis.

    maximize $3X + 2Y$
    subject to: $X \leq 6$
                 $X - Y \leq 2$
                 $X, Y \geq 0$

Converted to standard form, it becomes:

    maximize $3X + 2Y$
    subject to: $X + S1 = 6$
                 $X - Y + S2 = 2$
                 $X, Y, S1, S2 \geq 0$

The initial simplex tableau is:

C_B	C_j Basic Variables	3 X	2 Y	0 S1	0 S2	Solution	Ratio
0	S1	1	0	1	0	6	6
0	S2	①	-1	0	1	2	2
	Z_j	0	0	0	0	0	
	$C_j - Z_j$	3	2	0	0		

X is the entering variable; S2 is the leaving variable.

C_B	C_j Basic Variables	3 X	2 Y	0 S1	0 S2	Solution	Ratio
0	S1	0	①	1	-1	4	4
3	X	1	-1	0	1	2	-
	Z_j	3	-3	0	3	6	
	$C_j - Z_j$	0	5	0	-3		

Y is the entering variable; S1 is the leaving variable.

C_B	C_j Basic Variables	3 X	2 Y	0 S1	0 S2	Solution
2	Y	0	1	1	-1	4
3	X	1	0	1	0	6
	Z_j	3	2	5	-2	26
	$C_j - Z_j$	0	0	-5	2	

The $C_j - Z_j$ value for S2 is positive, indicating the potential for improvement, but the substitution coefficients above it are all ≤ 0, so the solution is unbounded.

c. Refer to page 32 for the model and analysis.

minimize $2X + 3Y$

subject to: $5X + 3Y \geq 15$

              $4X + 6Y \geq 24$

              $X, Y \geq 0$

Converted to standard form, it becomes:

minimize $2X + 3Y$ $+ MA1 + MA2$

subject to: $5X + 3Y - S1$ $+ A1$ $= 15$

              $4X + 6Y$ $- S2$ $+ A2 = 24$

              $X, Y, S1, S2, A1, A2 \geq 0$

The initial simplex tableau is:

C_B	Basic Variables	C_j 2 X	3 Y	0 S1	0 S2	M A1	M A2	Solution	Ratio
M	A1	⑤	3	-1	0	1	0	15	3
M	A2	4	6	0	-1	0	1	24	6
	Z_j	9M	9M	-M	-M	M	M	39M	
	$C_j - Z_j$	2-9M	3-9M	M	M	0	0		

X is the entering variable; A1 is the leaving variable.

C_B	Basic Variables	C_j 2 X	3 Y	0 S1	0 S2	M A1	M A2	Solution	Ratio
2	X	1	0.6	-.2	0	.2	0	3	5
M	A2	0	③.6	.8	-1	-.8	1	12	3.33
	Z_j	2	1.2+3.6M	-.4+.8M	-M	.4-.8M	M	6+12M	
	$C_j - Z_j$	0	1.8-3.6M	.4-.8M	M	-.4+1.8M	0		

Y is the entering variable; A2 is the leaving variable.

C_B	Basic Variables	C_j 2 X	3 Y	0 S1	0 S2	M A1	M A2	Solution	Ratio
2	X	1	0	-.333	.167	.333	-.167	1	-
3	Y	0	1	.222	-.278	.222	.278	3.333	15
	Z_j	2	3	0	-.5	0	.5	12.0	
	$C_j - Z_j$	0	0	0	.5	M	M-.5		

There is an <u>alternate optimum solution</u> indicated by the $C_j - Z_j$ value of zero for the nonbasic variable S1. Performing an additional pivot to bring S1 into the basis, replacing Y, gives the alternate extreme-point optimum.

45

C_B	C_j Basic Variables	2 X	3 Y	0 S1	0 S2	M A1	M A2	Solution
2	X	1	1.5	0	-.25	0	.25	6
0	S1	0	4.5	1	-1.2	-1	1.25	15
	Z_j	2	3	0	-.5	0	.5	12
	$C_j - Z_j$	0	0	0	.5	M	M-.5	

The two extreme point optima are:
  X = 1, Y = 3.333 and X = 6, S2 = 15

For both the value of the objective function is 12.

3. In standard form the problem is:

$$\text{maximize} \quad 11X_1 + 7X_2 + 1X_3$$

subject to:
$$5X_1 + 3X_2 + 1X_3 + S1 \qquad\qquad = 1000$$
$$4X_1 + 3X_2 + 2X_3 \qquad + S2 \qquad = 800$$
$$1X_1 + 2X_2 + 2X_3 \qquad\qquad + S3 = 400$$
$$X_1, X_2, X_3, S1, S2, S3 \geq 0$$

C_B	C_j Basic Variables	11 X1	7 X2	1 X3	0 S1	0 S2	0 S3	Solution	Ratio
0	S1	⑤	3	1	1	0	0	1000	200
0	S2	4	3	2	0	1	0	800	200
0	S3	1	2	2	0	0	1	400	400
	Z_j	0	0	0	0	0	0	0	
	$C_j - Z_j$	11	7	1	0	0	0		

X1 is the entering variable; S1 and S2 tie for the leaving variable.
Choose S1.

C_B	C_j Basic Variables	11 X1	7 X2	1 X3	0 S1	0 S2	0 S3	Solution	Ratio
11	X1	1	.6	.2	.2	0	0	200	333.33
0	S2	0	⑥	1.2	-.8	1	0	0	0
0	S3	0	1.4	1.8	-.2	0	1	200	142.86
	Z_j	11	6.6	2.2	2.2	0	0	2200	
	$C_j - Z_j$	0	.4	-1.2	-2.2	0	0		

X2 is the entering variable; S2 is the leaving variable. The solution
is, at this point, degenerate.

	C_j	11	7	1	0	0	0	
C_B	Basic Variables	X1	X2	X3	S1	S2	S3	Solution
11	X1	1	0	-1	1	-1	0	200
7	X2	0	1	2	-1.333	1.667	0	0
0	S3	0	0	-1	1.667	-2.333	1	200
	Z_j	11	7	3	1.667	.667	0	2200
	$C_j - Z_j$	0	0	-2	-1.667	-.667	0	

The optimal solution has been reached. It is degenerate.
$X_1 = 200$, $X_2 = 0$, S3 = 200, Objective Function = 2200

4. In standard form, the problem is:

maximize $22X_1 + 34X_2 + 23X_3 + 33X_4$ $- MA3 - MA4$

subject to:

$$4X_1 + 3X_2 \qquad\qquad\qquad + S1 \qquad\qquad = 48$$
$$5X_3 + 5X_4 + S2 \qquad\qquad = 40$$
$$1X_1 \qquad + 1X_3 \qquad\qquad - S3 + A3 \qquad = 13$$
$$1X_2 \qquad\qquad + 1X_4 - S4 \qquad + A4 = 7$$
$$X_1, X_2, X_3, X_4, S1, S2, S3, S4, A3, A4 \geqq 0$$

The tableaus for this problem are shown on pages 48 and 49. The optimal tableau is on page 49.

The optimal solution is:
$X_1 = 5$, $X_2 = 9.333$, $X_3 = 8$, S4 = 2.333, Objective Function = 611.333

Chapter Test

1. b	3. d	5. b	7. a	9. b
2. c	4. d	6. c	8. b	10. a

C_j		22	34	23	33	0	0	0	0	-M	-M		
C_B	Basic Variables	X1	X2	X3	X4	S1	S2	S3	S4	A3	A4	Solution	Ratio
0	S1	4	3	0	0	1	0	0	0	0	0	48	16
0	S2	0	0	5	5	0	1	0	0	0	0	40	–
-M	A3	1	0	1	0	0	0	-1	0	1	0	13	–
-M	A4	0	(1)	0	1	0	0	0	-1	0	1	7	7
	Z_j	-M	-M	-M	-M	0	0	M	M	-M	-M	-20M	
	C_j-Z_j	22+M	34+M	23+M	33+M	0	0	-M	-M	0	0		

The entering variable is X2; the leaving variable is A4.

C_B	Basic Variables	X1	X2	X3	X4	S1	S2	S3	S4	A3	A4	Solution	Ratio
0	S1	4	0	0	-3	1	0	0	3	0	-3	27	–
0	S2	0	0	(5)	5	0	1	0	0	0	0	40	8
-M	A3	1	0	1	0	0	0	-1	0	1	0	13	13
34	X2	0	1	0	1	0	0	0	-1	0	1	7	–
	Z_j	-M	34	-M	34	0	0	M	-34	-M	34	238-13M	
	C_j-Z_j	22+M	0	23+M	-1	0	0	-M	34	0	-34-M		

The entering variable is X3; the leaving variable is S2.

C_B	Basic Variables	X1	X2	X3	X4	S1	S2	S3	S4	A3	A4	Solution	Ratio
0	S1	4	0	0	-3	1	0	0	3	0	-3	27	6.75
23	X3	0	0	1	1	0	.2	0	0	0	0	8	–
-M	A3	(1)	0	0	-1	0	-.2	-1	0	1	0	5	5.00
34	X2	0	1	0	1	0	0	0	-1	0	1	7	–
	Z_j	-M	34	23	M+57	0	.2M+4.6	M	-34	-M	34	422-5M	
	C_j-Z_j	22+M	0	0	-24-M	0	-4.6-.2M	-M	34	0	-M-34		

The entering variable is X1; the leaving variable is A3.

C_B	Basic Variables	X1	X2	X3	X4	S1	S2	S3	S4	A3	A4	Solution	Ratio
0	S1	0	0	0	1	1	.8	4	(3)	-4	-3	7	2.333
23	X3	0	0	1	1	0	.2	0	0	0	0	8	–
22	X1	1	0	0	-1	0	-.2	-1	0	1	0	5	–
34	X2	0	1	0	1	0	0	0	-1	0	1	7	–
	Z_j	22	34	23	35	0	.2	-22	-34	22	34	532	
	C_j-Z_j	0	0	0	-2	0	-.2	22	34	-22-M	-34-M		

The entering variable is S4; the leaving variable is S1.

C_B	C_j →	22	34	23	33	0	0	0	0	-M	-M	
	Basic Variables	X1	X2	X3	X4	S1	S2	S3	S4	A3	A4	Solution
0	S4	0	0	0	.333	.333	.267	1.333	1	-1.333	-1	2.333
23	X3	0	0	1	1	0	.200	0	0	0	0	8
22	X1	1	0	0	-1	0	-.200	-1	0	1	0	5
34	X2	0	1	0	1.333	.333	.267	1.333	0	-1.333	0	9.333
	Z_j	22	34	23	46.333	11.333	9.267	23.333	0	-23.333	0	611.333
	$C_j - Z_j$	0	0	0	-13.333	-11.333	-9.267	-23.333	0	23.333-M	-M	

CHAPTER FIVE

SENSITIVITY ANALYSIS

MAIN POINTS

1. After formulating an LP model and solving it, a third phase, <u>sensitivity analysis</u> or <u>postoptimality analysis</u>, is usually conducted. The purpose of this analysis is to determine how sensitive the solution to the problem is to the coefficient values used.

2. In many cases the coefficient values used in the model are estimates. In other cases, even if the values used can be considered to be accurate, they will change over time. In either case, it is important to know by how much the coefficient would have to change before it would affect the solution and what that effect would be.

3. Sensitivity analysis is also a tool for flexibility planning, helpful in generating alternatives for the decision maker to choose from and useful in planning for response to unpredictable changes in the decision conditions.

4. Every LP problem (a <u>primal</u> problem) has a counterpart called the <u>dual</u> problem. The solution values for the dual problem are <u>shadow prices</u> which tell us something about the marginal value of limited resources or the marginal cost of constraints.

5. To form the dual problem for an LP, the first step is to make sure that the original or primal problem is in the correct form. If the primal problem is a maximization, all constraints must be $\leq$ or =, even if that makes the right-hand-side values negative. If the primal problem is a minimization, all constraints must be $\geq$ or =.

6. The dual problem is then formed by flip-flopping or reversing the primal.
    a. Form the dual objective function by using the primal right-hand-side values.
    b. Use the primal objective function coefficients as the dual right-hand-side values.
    c. Form the ith dual constraint from the coefficients of variable i in the primal, reversing the direction of the inequalities unless the original variable was unrestricted in sign, in which case the dual constraint is an equation. If the primal constraint was an equation, its dual variable is unrestricted in sign.
    d. If the primal is a maximization, the dual is a minimization, and vice versa.

7. Each primal variable has a dual constraint and each primal constraint has a dual variable. The value of this dual variable, the shadow price, represents the marginal value or cost of its associated primal constraint. Its value is the amount by which the value of the primal objective function will be improved (worsened) for each unit, within some range, by which the right-hand-side value of that constraint is loosened

51

(tightened). Specifically, if the constraint is a resource limit in a problem involving the maximization of profits, the shadow price tells how much additional profit can be realized if one additional unit of that resource was available.

8. The dual variable values can be found in the primal problem's final simplex tableau. They are the absolute values of the C_j-Z_j values under the columns corresponding to the constraint slack variables. For an equality constraint, which has no slack, it is found by dropping the M from the C_j-Z_j under the artificial variable.

9. Shadow prices are extremely useful for analyzing the potential effect of changing the right-hand-side values. If a resource constraint has slack, its shadow price is zero. This indicates that there is no value to getting more and no cost to giving up some of what is available since the optimal solution does not use all that is available anyway. If the constraint is met as an equation, however, there might be value to getting more or a loss if some had to be given up. The shadow price measures this value or cost, showing by how much the objective function will increase, for one additional unit of the resource, or decrease for one unit less. Assuming that the normal cost of this resource has been recognized in determining the decision variables' profit contributions, this shadow price then represents the maximum premium above the normal cost that the decision maker should pay to get an additional unit.

10. A shadow price measures marginal value, but it is valid only over a specified range. The number of units which can be added (or taken away) from that constraint's right-hand-side value before the shadow price will change can be determined by right-hand-side ranging. The objective of right-hand-side ranging is to determine the range within which the current basis remains optimal and the shadow prices remain valid. Note that as the right-hand-side value changes the values of the optimal solution variables will change, but which variables are in the solution may not.

11. Changing the right-hand-side value of a constraint is equivalent to introducing positive or negative slack into that constraint. Given that, the range within which the current basis remains optimal can be determined by finding how much positive or negative slack could be introduced into the solution before one of the current basic variables would reach zero. Making the slack positive is equivalent to lowering the right-hand-side value, so the maximum reduction in the right-hand-side value is found by using the smallest ratio of solution value to positive substitution coefficient for the slack variable of the constraint. The maximum increase in the right-hand-side value is found by using the smallest absolute value of the ratios of the solution value to the negative substitution coefficients for that slack variable.

12. If we wish to consider whether a new variable would have any effect on the currently optimal solution, we can check using the shadow prices. Each constraint's coefficient for the new variable is multiplied by that constraint's shadow price and the sum is found. This is the equivalent of Z_j. If C_j-Z_j is less than zero for a maximization (or greater than zero for a minimization), the new variable would not be in the optimal solution.

13. Sensitivity analysis for objective function coefficients breaks into two parts, for nonbasic and basic variables. A nonbasic variable's objective function coefficient C_j can be changed until the C_j-Z_j value in the final tableau would change sign (i.e., it can change in one direction by the amount of its opportunity loss or reduced cost and to infinity in the other direction).

14. Changes in basic variable coefficients are more difficult because they may affect all C_j-Z_j values. The general rule is that a basic variable's C_j can change as long as no variable's C_j-Z_j changes sign. This can be checked by taking ratios of the C_j-Z_j values to the substitution coefficients in the row for the basic variable of interest. The minimum positive ratio gives the maximum increase possible and the absolute value of the least negative ratio gives the maximum decrease possible. Some modification of these rules is necessary if there are alternate optima.

15. Most standard LP computer packages contain procedures for doing the sensitivity analysis on the right-hand-side values and objective function coefficients. They are provided either automatically or on request.

KEY TERMS

Match each term with the appropriate definition below.

<u>Terms</u>

_____ 1. dual problem

_____ 2. objective-function-
         coefficient ranging

_____ 3. primal problem

_____ 4. right-hand-side ranging

_____ 5. sensitivity analysis

_____ 6. shadow price

<u>Definitions</u>

A. The LP model developed to solve the problem as originally posed.

B. Determination of the effect on the LP solution of changing the values of coefficients in the model.

C. The LP model developed by flip-flopping the role of the coefficients in the original problem.

D. Determination of the amount by which a variable's cost or gain can change in either direction before changing the optimal solution.

E. The marginal value of relaxing or tightening a constraint.

F. Determination of the amount by which a constraint's boundary value can change before the basis and the constraint's shadow price would change.

Recall the Blackwell Manufacturing Co. product mix problem (Review Exercise 1, Chapter 2, page 13). The formulation of the problem and the LINDO solution output are shown below.

```
MAX        10 A + 12 B
SUBJECT TO
    2)    2 A + 6 B <=    30      Dept. T hours
    3)    5 A + 4 B <=    40      Dept. P hours
    4)    6 A + 4 B <=    60      Material
END

LP OPTIMUM FOUND AT STEP          2

            OBJECTIVE FUNCTION VALUE

    1)       92.7272700

    VARIABLE          VALUE              REDUCED COST
        A            5.454545              .000000
        B            3.181818              .000000


        ROW    SLACK OR SURPLUS       DUAL PRICES
        2)         .000000              .909091
        3)         .000000             1.636364
        4)       14.545450              .000000

NO. ITERATIONS=         2

RANGES IN WHICH THE BASIS IS UNCHANGED:

                            OBJ COEFFICIENT RANGES
    VARIABLE       CURRENT       ALLOWABLE        ALLOWABLE
                    COEF         INCREASE         DECREASE
        A        10.000000       5.000000         6.000000
        B        12.000000      18.000000         4.000000

                            RIGHTHAND SIDE RANGES
        ROW        CURRENT       ALLOWABLE        ALLOWABLE
                    RHS          INCREASE         DECREASE
        2        30.000000      30.000000        14.000000
        3        40.000000      11.428570        20.000000
        4        60.000000       INFINITY        14.545450
```

a. What is the optimal solution and associated profit?

b. Which constraints are binding?

c. Which production resource(s) would you recommend for expansion and why?

d. A change in suppliers will cause the profit contribution of B to drop to $7.50. What can you say about the current solution?

e. Over what range can the availability of material vary before the basis changes?

f. What happens in part (e) if the RHS changes to a value outside the specified range?

g. Consider a new product C. It requires 3 hours in Department T, 5 hours in Department P, and 5 units of material. What would the profit contribution have to be in order for Blackwell to produce Product C?

h. Consider a simultaneous decrease in Department T time of 7 hours and a 5-hour increase in Department P time available. Can you make any conclusions concerning a basis change or the new optimal solution?

Solution

a. Reading the LINDO output, we can see that the optimal solution is to produce 5.45 As and 3.18 Bs. The associated profit is 92.72.

b. The first two constraints on Departments T and P are binding since they have zero slack.

c. Since the third constraint already has slack, the material resource is not a candidate for expansion. Departments T or P are candidates for expansion since their shadow prices are greater than zero. If the objective function coefficients take into account the variable cost of Departments T and P time, then either could be expanded with Department P being favored with the larger shadow price of 1.63. However, if the costs of procuring additional time in Department T or Department P are not reflected in the objective function coefficients, then the cost of obtaining each of these additional hours in Departments T and P must be subtracted from 0.909 and 1.63, respectively. In this case, it is highly unlikely that it would be worthwhile to expand either department.

d. A decrease in profit of Product B from 12 to 7.5 is outside the relevant range. Thus, the current basis and solution would no longer be optimal. However, the solution would still be feasible but the profit would decrease to 78.409. To obtain the new optimal solution, the model would need to be resolved with the new objective function coefficient of 7.5.

e. Looking at the RHS ranging output, we can see that the allowable decrease is 14.54545 and the increase is unbounded. Thus, the range is 60-14.54545 to infinity or $[45.45455, \infty)$.

f. A basis change and new solution is required since the current solution would no longer be feasible much less optimal. At least one of the basic variables would have a negative value.

g. Considering the marginal values of the three resources and multiplying these values (shadow prices) times the number of units needed yields:

$$3 \times 0.909091$$
$$5 \times 1.636364$$
$$\underline{5 \times 0}$$
$$Z_c = 10.909091$$

55

Thus, Product C must yield a profit contribution of at least 10.91 before it is worth producing.

h. To consider simultaneous changes in the objective function coefficients or RHS values requires the application of the 100 percent rule. Calculating the percentage changes relative to the allowable yields:

$$7/14 + 5/11.42857 = 0.50 + 0.4375 = 0.9375$$

Since $0.9375 < 1.0$, the basis would not change. Using the shadow prices, we can calculate the new profit of

$$92.72727 + 5(1.636364) - 7(0.909091) = 94.545453$$

However, obtaining the solution values of A and B would require resolving the model using LINDO.

REVIEW EXERCISES

1. Formulate the dual problem for:

maximize $\quad 5X_1 + 4X_2 + 7X_3$

subject to: $\quad 6X_1 + 2X_2 + 3X_3 \leq 25$

$\qquad\qquad\quad 4X_1 + 4X_2 + X_3 \leq 18$

$\qquad\qquad\quad 2X_1 + 3X_2 - X_3 \geq 6$

$\qquad\qquad\qquad X_1, X_2, X_3 \geq 0$

2. Formulate the dual problem for:

minimize $\quad 8X_1 + 6X_2 - 4X_3$

subject to: $\quad X_1 + 4X_2 + 3X_3 \geq 10$

$\qquad\qquad\quad 7X_1 + 3X_2 + X_3 \geq 15$

$\qquad\qquad\quad 4X_1 + 3X_2 + 4X_3 = 20$

$\qquad\qquad\qquad X_1, X_2, X_3 \geq 0$

*3. A company manufactures two products, A and B. To manufacture product A requires four hours of labor and uses three pounds of raw material. Product B requires three hours of labor and six pounds of raw material. There are 24 hours of labor and 30 pounds of raw material available. In addition to the limits imposed by these resources, the marketing department does not believe that any more than four units of B can be sold. A unit of product A returns $16 in profit, a unit of B returns $20.

The LP model for maximizing total profits is:

maximize $\quad 16A + 20B$

subject to: $\quad 4A + 3B \leq 24 \quad$ (Labor)

$\qquad\qquad\quad 3A + 6B \leq 30 \quad$ (Material)

$\qquad\qquad\qquad\quad B \leq 4 \quad$ (Demand)

$\qquad\qquad\quad A, B \geq 0$

56

Use a graphical method to solve the problem and answer the following questions:
a. What is the shadow price for Labor?
b. Over what range does it hold?
c. What is the shadow price for Material?
d. Over what range does it hold?
e. What is the shadow price for Demand?
f. Over what range does it hold?
g. By how much can the profit of A increase and decrease before the optimal solution would change?
h. By how much can the profit of B increase and decrease before the optimal solution would change?

In all cases, assume that only the one coefficient is changed.

4. Confirm your answers to Exercise 3 by solving the problem with the simplex method. In addition, answer the following question:

Company management is considering a new product that would require two (2) hours of labor and five (5) pounds of material, having a profit of $15. Would this new product change the solution? What is the minimum profit that would be required to make this product of interest?

*5. A dog food manufacturer combines three standard foods to make a mixture. The standard foods used have characteristics as given in the table, with maximum or minimum limits for the combination being as specified.

Characteristic	Standard Food			Required
	1	2	3	
Protein	25 percent	40 percent	35 percent	30 (min)
Fat	10 percent	6 percent	8 percent	7 (min)
Fiber	4 percent	5 percent	6 percent	6 (max)
Ash	8 percent	4 percent	12 percent	8 (max)
Moisture	10 percent	8 percent	8 percent	10 (max)
Cost/lb.	$0.25	$0.32	$0.24	

The manufacturer wishes to blend the three standard foods to make 100-pound bags of the mixture. An LP model to minimize the cost of doing this is:

$$\text{minimize} \quad 25X_1 + 32X_2 + 24X_3$$

$$
\begin{aligned}
\text{subject to:} \quad 25X_1 + 40X_2 + 35X_3 &\geq 30 \quad \text{Protein} \\
10X_1 + 6X_2 + 8X_3 &\geq 7 \quad \text{Fat} \\
4X_1 + 5X_2 + 6X_3 &\leq 6 \quad \text{Fiber} \\
8X_1 + 4X_2 + 12X_3 &\leq 8 \quad \text{Ash} \\
10X_1 + 8X_2 + 8X_3 &\leq 10 \quad \text{Moisture} \\
X_1 + X_2 + X_3 &= 100 \quad \text{Weight} \\
X_1, X_2, X_3 &\geq 0
\end{aligned}
$$

The final simplex tableau for this problem is (the columns for the artificial variables for the Protein and Fat constraints (A1 and A2) were dropped since they are simply the negatives of the S1 and S2 columns):

C_B	Basic Variables	C_j 25	32	24	0	0	0	0	0	M	Solution
		X1	X2	X3	S1	S2	S3	S4	S5	A6	
32	X2	0	1	0	-4	0	0	-10	0	-.2	20
25	X1	1	0	0	8	0	0	-5	0	3.4	60
0	S3	0	0	0	.12	0	1	-.2	0	.006	1.4
24	X3	0	0	1	-4	0	0	15	0	-2.2	20
0	S5	0	0	0	-.16	0	0	.10	1	-.148	.8
0	S2	0	0	0	.24	1	0	.10	0	.152	1.8
	Z_j	25	32	24	-24	0	0	0	0	25.8	2620
	$C_j - Z_j$	0	0	0	24	0	0	85	0	M-25.8	

a. What would it cost to increase the Protein content to 31 pounds (31%)?

b. For how many additional pounds would this be true?

c. How much would be saved by increasing the Ash content to 9 pounds (9%)?

d. For how many pounds increase would this be true?

e. Within what cost range for Standard Food 1 is this solution optimal?

f. Repeat (e) for Standard Food 2.

CHAPTER TEST

1. Which of the following statements is not true?
   a. Most LP problems have an associated dual problem.
   b. The dual of the dual is the primal.
   c. The dual problem variables are the marginal costs or values of constraints.
   d. The value of a variable that is unrestricted in sign can be found as the difference of two nonnegative variables.

2. Which of the following statements is true?
   a. All dual problems are minimizations.
   b. For both primal and dual problems all variables must be nonnegative.
   c. The optimal solutions for both the primal and dual problems can be found in either problem's final simplex tableau.
   d. The dual problem cannot be formulated if the primal problem has both $\leq$ and $\geq$ constraints.

3. The values of the dual variables are found in the final primal tableau:
   a. in the "Solution" column.
   b. under their associated decision variables in the $C_j - Z_j$ row.
   c. under their associated constraints' slack or artificial variables in the $C_j - Z_j$ row.
   d. they are not found in the primal tableau.

4. If a primal problem has an equality constraint, its associated dual variable's value is:
   a. positive.
   b. zero.
   c. negative.
   d. any of the above.

5. If in the final solution to an LP problem a constraint is met as a strict inequality, its shadow price is:
   a. positive.
   b. zero.
   c. negative.
   d. any of the above.

6. In an LP problem set up to maximize contribution to profit and overhead, the shadow price for a resource limit constraint tells:
   a. by how much the objective function will increase if the resource limit is lowered by one unit.
   b. by how much the objective function will increase if the resource limit is raised by one unit.
   c. how much more of the resource can be profitably used.
   d. how much of the resource can be given up before the solution will change.

7. Sensitivity analysis is used to evaluate or determine:
   a. the effect on the solution of changing an objective function coefficient.
   b. the amount by which a resource limit can be changed without affecting the basic solution.
   c. whether a new variable would be active in the solution.
   d. all of the above.

Questions 8 through 10 relate to the following problem: A company manufactures three products: Product 1, Product 2, and Product 3. The manufacture of these products requires processing in two departments, assembly and packaging. An LP model to maximize contribution to profit and overhead is:

$$\text{maximize} \quad 5X_1 + 6X_2 + 2X_3$$
$$\text{subject to:} \quad 2X_1 + 3X_2 + X_3 \leq 27 \quad \text{(Assembly)}$$
$$2X_1 + X_2 + X_3 \leq 18 \quad \text{(Packaging)}$$
$$X_1, X_2, X_3 \geq 0$$

The final simplex tableau for this problem is:

C_B	Basic Variables	C_j 5	6	2	0	0	Solution
		X1	X2	X3	S1	S2	
6	X2	0	1	0	.5	-.5	4.50
5	X1	1	0	.5	-.25	.75	6.75
	z_j	5	6	2.5	1.75	.75	60.75
	$c_j - z_j$	0	0	-.5	-1.75	-.75	

8. One additional unit of assembly time would enable the company to increase their contribution to profit and overhead by:
   a. 1.75.
   b. .75.
   c. .50.
   d. 0.

9. The number of additional units that would be worth this amount is:
   a. 9.
   b. 27.
   c. 1.
   d. 7.

10. The maximum amount by which the profit contribution of Product 1 (objective function coefficient of X_1) can be <u>reduced</u> before the optimal solution would change is:
    a. 2.333.
    b. 1.0.
    c. 5.0.
    d. It cannot be reduced.

ANSWER KEY

<u>Terms</u>

1. C	3. A	5. B
2. D	4. F	6. E

<u>Review Exercises</u>

1. First reverse the order of the third inequality so all inequalities are ≤:

$$\text{maximize} \quad 5X_1 + 4X_2 + 7X_3$$
$$\text{subject to:} \quad 6X_1 + 2X_2 + 3X_3 \leq 25$$
$$4X_1 + 4X_2 + X_3 \leq 18$$
$$-2X_1 - 3X_2 + X_3 \leq -6$$

   The dual problem is:

$$\text{minimize} \quad 25Y_1 + 18Y_2 - 6Y_3$$
$$\text{subject to:} \quad 6Y_1 + 4Y_2 - 2Y_3 \geq 5$$
$$2Y_1 + 4Y_2 - 3Y_3 \geq 4$$
$$3Y_1 + Y_2 + Y_3 \geq 7$$
$$Y_1, Y_2, Y_3 \geq 0$$

2. The primal problem is already in standard form.

   The dual problem is:

maximize $10Y_1 + 15Y_2 + 20Y_3$

subject to: $Y_1 + 7Y_2 + 4Y_3 \leqq 8$

$4Y_1 + 3Y_2 + 3Y_3 \leqq 6$

$3Y_1 + Y_2 + 4Y_3 \leqq -4$

$Y_1, Y_2 \geqq 0$

Y_3 unrestricted in sign

In order to solve the problem the third constraint would be reversed to have a positive right-hand side and the unrestricted variable Y_3 would be replaced by the difference of two nonnegative variables. The resulting dual problem is:

minimize $10Y_1 + 15Y_2 + 20Y_3^+ - 20Y_3^-$

subject to: $Y_1 + 7Y_2 + 4Y_3^+ - 4Y_3^- \leqq 8$

$4Y_1 + 3Y_2 + 3Y_3^+ - 3Y_3^- \leqq 6$

$-3Y_1 - Y_2 - 4Y_3^+ + 4Y_3^- \geqq 4$

$Y_1, Y_2, Y_3^+, Y_3^- \geqq 0$

3. The diagram for the optimal solution to the problem is:

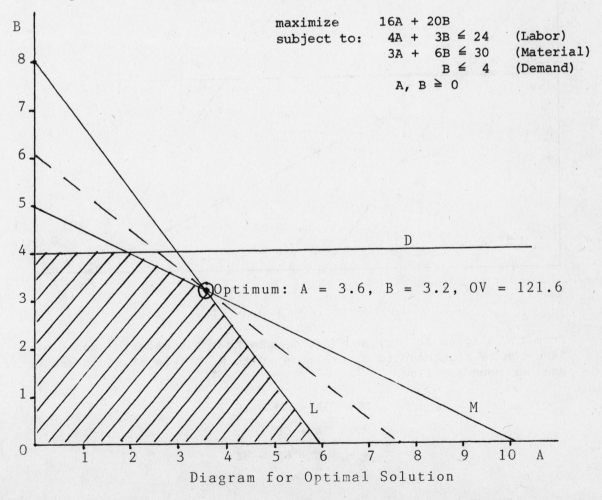

maximize $16A + 20B$

subject to: $4A + 3B \leqq 24$ (Labor)

$3A + 6B \leqq 30$ (Material)

$B \leqq 4$ (Demand)

$A, B \geqq 0$

Optimum: A = 3.6, B = 3.2, OV = 121.6

Diagram for Optimal Solution

61

From the diagram for (a) and (b) below, we see that the labor constraint line can be tightened to L_1 or loosened to L_2 before it would encounter another boundary line and change the nature of the basis and thus the shadow price.

$$L_1: \quad 4A + 3B = 20$$
$$L: \quad 4A + 3B = 24$$
$$L_2: \quad 4A + 3B = 40$$

By reducing the RHS of L to 20, the value of the objective function is reduced from 121.6 to 112. The shadow price is, therefore:

$$\text{Shadow price for Labor} = \frac{121.6 - 112}{24 - 20} = \frac{9.6}{4} = 2.40$$

and holds within the range: $20 \leq \text{Labor Available} \leq 40$.

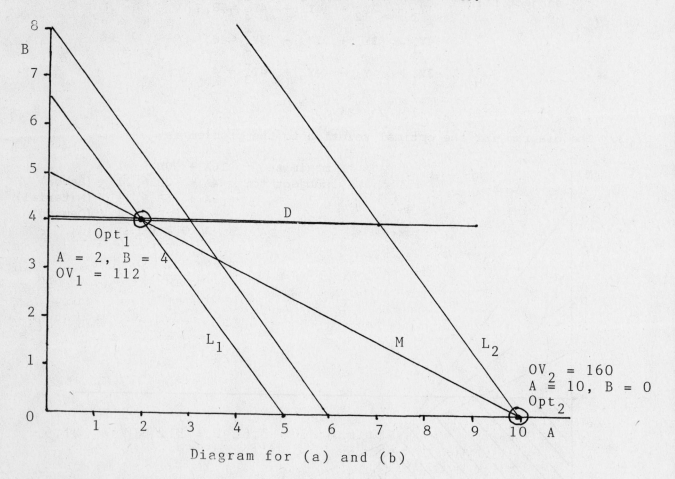

Diagram for (a) and (b)

From the diagram for (c) and (d), we see that the material constraint line can be tightened to M_1 or loosened to M_2 before it would encounter another boundary line.

$$M_1: \quad 3A + 6B = 18$$
$$M: \quad 3A + 6B = 30$$
$$M_2: \quad 3A + 6B = 33$$

62

By reducing the RHS of M to 18, the value of the objective function is reduced from 121.6 to 96. The shadow price is, therefore:

$$\text{Shadow Price for Material} = \frac{121.6 - 96}{30 - 18} = \frac{25.6}{12} = 2.133$$

and it holds within the range: $18 \leq \text{Material Available} \leq 33$.

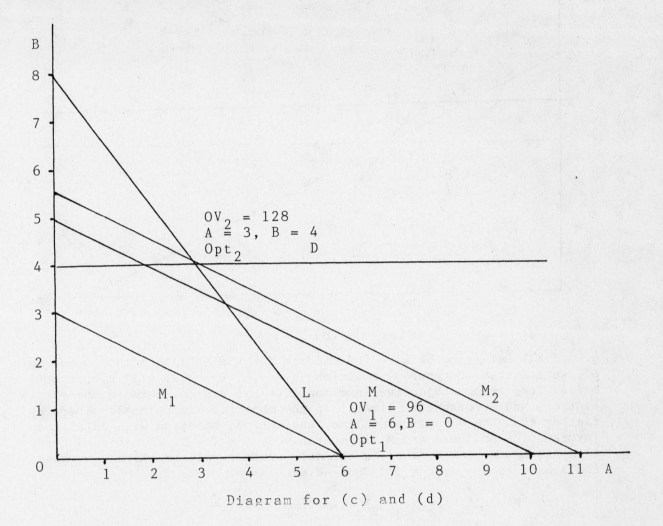

Diagram for (c) and (d)

From the diagram for (e) and (f), we see that the demand constraint line is not binding in the original problem. Thus it can be tightened to D_1 before it encounters the previously optimal solution and can be loosened without limit (there is no D_2).

$$D_1: \quad B = 3.2$$
$$D: \quad B = 4$$

Since reducing the RHS of D to 3.2 does not change the value of the objective function, the shadow price is:

$$\text{Shadow Price for Demand} = 0$$

and holds as long as: $\text{Demand} \geq 3.2$.

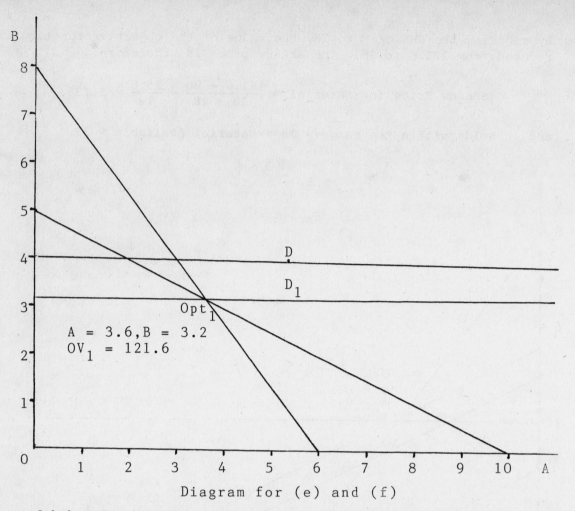

Diagram for (e) and (f)

g. and h.) Referring back to the diagram for the optimal solution on page 61, we see that the present solution (A = 3.6, B = 3.2) will remain optimal as long as the objective function line has a slope between the slopes of the L and M constraint lines. If the objective function line becomes flatter than the M constraint line, the optimal solution will be at the intersection of the D and M lines at A = 2, B = 4. If it becomes steeper than the L constraint line the optimal solution will be where L crosses the A axis at A = 6, B = 0. Thus we must have:

(from M) $(3/6) \leqq (C_A/C_B) \leqq (4/3)$ (from L)

Holding C_B fixed at 20, we get:

$$(3/6) \leqq (C_A/20) \leqq (4/3)$$

and $10 \leqq C_A \leqq 26.667.$

Holding C_A fixed at 16, we get:

(from L) $(4/3) \geqq (16/C_B) \geqq (3/6)$ (from M)

$$(3/4) \leqq (C_B/16) \leqq (6/3)$$

and $12 \leqq C_B \leqq 32.$

64

4. The final simplex tableau is:

CB	Basic Variables	A	B	S1	S2	S3	Solution
0	S3	0	0	.2	-.267	1	.8
16	A	1	0	.4	-.200	0	3.6
20	B	0	1	-.2	.267	0	3.2
	Z_j	16	20	2.4	2.133	0	121.6
	$C_j - Z_j$	0	0	-2.4	-2.133	0	

a. The shadow price for Labor is found under the S1 column as the negative of the $C_j - Z_j$ value: <u>2.4</u>

b. The maximum decrease in the Labor availability is found as the smallest ratio of solution value to positive substitution coefficient in the S1 column:

$$\min \left(\frac{.8}{.2}, \frac{3.6}{.4}\right) = 4$$

so the maximum decrease is 4 units.

The maximum increase is the smallest absolute value of solution value to negative substitution coefficient ratio:

$$\left|\frac{3.2}{-.2}\right| = 16$$

The range over which the shadow price holds is, therefore:

$$24 - 4 = \underline{20} \quad \text{to} \quad 24 + 16 = \underline{40}.$$

c. The shadow price for Material is <u>2.133</u>.

d. The maximum decrease for the material right-hand side is:

$$\frac{3.2}{.267} = 12$$

The maximum increase is:

$$\min \left(\left|\frac{.8}{.2687}\right|, \left|\frac{3.6}{-.2}\right|\right) = 3$$

The range for the right-hand side of the material constraint is, therefore:

$$30 - 12 = \underline{18} \quad \text{to} \quad 30 + 3 = \underline{33}.$$

e. The shadow price for Demand is <u>0</u> since there is slack in the constraint.

f. The zero shadow price is valid if the right-hand side is greater than the amount actually being used, which is 4 - .8 = <u>3.2</u>.

g. The maximum decrease in C_A is given by the smallest negative ratio of $C_j - Z_j$ to the substitution coefficients in the A row, which is:

$$\frac{-2.4}{.4} = -6.$$

The maximum increase in C_A is given by the smallest positive ratio, which is:

$$\frac{-2.133}{-.20} = 10.67.$$

This gives a range for C_A of:

$$16 - 6 = \underline{10} \quad \text{to} \quad 16 + 10.67 = \underline{26.67}.$$

h. The maximum decrease in C_B is:

$$\frac{-2.133}{.267} = -.8$$

and the maximum increase in C_B is:

$$\frac{-2.40}{-.20} = 12$$

which gives a range for C_B of:

$$20 - 8 = \underline{12} \quad \text{to} \quad 20 + 12 = \underline{32}.$$

i. To determine whether the new product would be active in the optimal solution we multiply the constraint coefficients for the product times the constraint shadow prices, sum, and compare to the profit value.

(Labor)	2(2.40)
(Material)	+ 5(2.133)
(Demand)	+ 0(0)
	15.467 = Z

Since Z = 15.467 exceeds the profit of 15, the variable would <u>not</u> be active. The minimum profit for this product to be produced is 15.467.

5.

a. The shadow price for the Protein constraint is <u>24</u> cents.

b. Raising the right-hand side of a $\geq$ constraint is equivalent to introducing slack at a positive level. (Remember that the slack is <u>subtracted</u> so to have the left side equal to a larger value we subtract something to make it equal to 30.) We thus look for the smallest ratio of solution value to <u>positive</u> substitution coefficient.

$$\min \left(\frac{60}{8}, \frac{1.4}{.12}, \frac{1.8}{.24}\right) = 7.5$$

We can raise the Protein requirement by up to 7.5 units to 37.5 at a shadow price of 24 cents per unit.

c. The shadow price of Ash (a $\leq$ constraint) is <u>85</u> cents.

d. This is equivalent to introducing <u>negative</u> slack since we are raising the right-hand side of a = constraint. The maximum increase is the minimum absolute value of the ratio of solution value to <u>negative</u> substitution coefficient.

$$\min \left(\left| \frac{20}{-10} \right|, \left| \frac{60}{-5} \right|, \left| \frac{1.4}{-.2} \right| \right) = 2$$

The constraint can be raised to 8 + 2 = <u>10</u> at a savings of 85 cents per unit.

e. The maximum increase is given by

$$\frac{24}{8} = 3$$

from the S1 column and the maximum decrease is given by

$$\frac{85}{-5} = -17$$

from the S4 column, looking at substitution coefficients in the X_1 row. This gives a range for C_1 of:

25 -17 = <u>8</u> to 25 + 3 = <u>28.</u>

f. The maximum decrease is the <u>least</u> negative of:

$$\frac{24}{-4}, \frac{85}{-10} = -6$$

for a lower limit of 32 - 6 = <u>26</u>. Since there is no positive substitution coefficient, there is no upper limit. The range for C_2 is thus:

26 to unlimited

Chapter Test

1. a   3. c   5. b   7. d   9. a
2. c   4. d   6. b   8. a   10. b

CHAPTER SIX

DISTRIBUTION AND ASSIGNMENT PROBLEMS

MAIN POINTS

1. There are several types of LP models that, due to their special structure, have specialized solution procedures that are more efficient than the regular simplex method. Three such models are the transportation, transshipment, and assignment models.

2. The advantages of the specialized algorithms for these problems are:
a. computations are 100 to 150 times as fast;
b. computer storage needs are much less, permitting larger problems to be solved; and
c. the solutions are integer if specific parameters are also integer.

3. One approach to solving these problems is to use a heuristic solution procedure, a method that will in general provide a very good solution in a short time using rules of thumb or solution guidelines. The disadvantages of heuristics are that they do not guarantee a feasible or an optimal solution. There is no way of knowing how good the heuristic solution is. Heuristics do, however, make it possible to solve some very large, complex problems that are too difficult to solve with algorithms. For the transportation problem, the heuristics also provide a very good starting point for the optimization procedures.

4. The transportation problem is also known as the Hitchcock - Koopmans transportation problem, after its formulators, or the distribution problem. These names come from the original impetus to this model, determining the minimum cost way to distribute or transport material from a number of sources where it is available to a set of destinations where it is required.

5. The assumptions necessary to apply the transportation model are:
a. units of a homogeneous product (which does not have to be a thing, it could be a capacity to do something) are available at
b. sources, of which there are m, in quantities $a_1, \ldots, a_m$, and are required at
c. destinations, of which there are n, in quantities $b_1, \ldots, b_n$
d. the cost of shipping a unit from source i to destination j is given by C_{ij} and is independent of the amount shipped on that route (i.e., the total route shipping cost is linear).
e. for the specialized solution procedure, it is further required that the sum of the availabilities equals the sum of the requirements.

6. To use the specialized transportation model solution procedures, the problem is formulated using a transportation tableau, a rectangular matrix. There is one row for each source, with the availability written to its right, and one column for each destination, with its requirement written below it. In the upper left corner of a cell in the tableau is written the unit cost of shipping from that cell's row source to its

column destination. In solving the problem, a second entry will be made in some cells, the values of the decision variables, the amounts to ship on the source-destination route.

7. One transportation problem heuristic is the <u>row minimum</u> method. Computational studies have shown that this procedure not only gives good approximate solutions, but also, in combination with the MODI optimization method, can solve transportation problems to optimality faster than any other procedure.

8. The row minimum method starts by using the minimum cost cell in row 1, assigning to that cell the lower of what is available in the row and required in the column. The amount assigned is subtracted from both the row availability and column requirement. Whichever was used up (row or column) is crossed out. If both are used up, cross out the column. Move to the second row and repeat the process, ignoring any cells in crossed out columns. When all rows have been done, return to the first row not crossed out and repeat the process. Keep doing this until all rows and columns are crossed out. The result will be a heuristic solution to the problem and a starting point for MODI.

9. The <u>Vogel Approximation Method</u> or <u>VAM</u> technique generally gives lower cost solutions than the row minimum method but is more complex and time consuming. It is a "look ahead" method using <u>opportunity costs</u>. The basic idea is to use cells that will avoid the use of other cells with high costs. The opportunity loss for not using a cell is estimated as the difference between the cell's cost and the next lowest cost in its row or column. For each row and column the difference between its two lowest cost cells is recorded. The row or column with the greatest opportunity loss is selected for use. The lowest cost cell in that row or column is filled as described in (8) and the use is subtracted from the row availability and column requirement. The one used up is crossed out, new opportunity losses are computed, and the process repeats. This is done until there is only one row or column left. At that point, the remaining cells are filled as needed.

10. The transportation model is useful for situations other than problems of transporting materials. One other popular use is for production scheduling and inventory planning. In this case, the sources and destinations refer to time periods and the costs are a combination of unit production and inventory carrying charges.

11. The transportation model can be used to maximize gains as well as to minimize costs. Two ways to do this are: (1) multiply all gains by -1 and minimize the negative of the original objective function, and (2) reverse the decision rules, looking for the largest gains (rather than the smallest costs) in the row <u>maximum</u> or VAM starting rule and using the most <u>positive</u> cell evaluator in MODI, stopping when all evaluators are less than or equal to zero.

12. The <u>transshipment</u> problem is a variation of the transportation problem, solved with the standard transportation problem algorithm. Nodes in the network are divided into three groups: sources - which supply the units, sinks - which absorb them, and transshipment points - which receive from sources or other transshipment points and send to the sinks or other transshipment points. In developing a transportation model for solving a

transshipment problem, the transshipment points are treated as both sources (rows) and destinations (columns). Transshipment problems are useful in analyzing distribution systems with intermediate points between the supplies and demands.

13. Transshipment network models are very useful because they allow analysts to model a much broader range of problems, such as the distribution system of the Agrico Chemical Company as presented in the chapter of the text.

14. The transshipment network is mathematically modeled by forcing a conservation of flow at each node of the network. Thus, a constraint requires:

   total flow out - total flow in = node supply (demand)

   Supplies are positive quantities while demands are negative.

15. The assignment problem involves matching, on a one-to-one basis, the members of two sets. These are often jobs to be done and people or machines to do them, the problem being to assign each job to a person so that each job is done by one person and each person does one job.

16. The assignment model is valuable, not only for problems that fit the requirements, but also as a submodel within other kinds of problems. An example of this is the travelling salesman problem.

17. Network models including transportation, transshipment, and assignment models are so efficient that some analysts have advocated the netform concept. The idea is to exploit the network substructure of large-scale linear and integer programming models. In some cases, this has led to much faster solution procedures and solutions to previously unsolvable problems.

Supplement Main Points

18. The steps in solving a transportation problem are just like the steps in using the simplex method to solve regular LP problems.
   a. Find an initial solution (using row minimum or VAM).
   b. Check it for optimality.
   c. If not optimal, determine the incoming variable.
   d. Determine the leaving variable.
   e. Update the tableau and return to (b).

19. The check for optimality and the updating can be done with the modified distribution or MODI method. The optimality checking involves finding row and column evaluators and involves solving the equations of the dual problem.

20. Although, as an LP problem, the transportation model has m+n constraints (m sources and n destinations), because the constraints are all equalities and $\Sigma a_i = \Sigma b_j$, there are only m+n-1 independent constraints and m+n-1 variables or cells in the solution. We find m row evaluators, R_i, and n column evaluators, K_j, that satisfy the m+n-1 equations, $R_i + K_j = C_{ij}$, for the cells in the solution. Because there is one more variable than equation, the solution is not unique. However, if we set one evaluator equal to any arbitrarily chosen value, we can solve uniquely for the rest. The easiest thing to do is set $R_1 = 0$ and solve for the others.

21. Once the R_i and K_j are found, the unused cells (nonbasic variables) can be evaluated by computing $C_{ij} - R_i - K_j$. This is equivalent to finding $C_j - Z_j$ in regular LP. If they are all greater than or equal to zero, a minimum has been reached.

22. If the current solution is not optimal, pick the cell with the most negative evaluator as the incoming variable. Find a closed loop or cycle consisting of that cell and used or occupied cells (basic variables). In forming a cycle or loop, start with the cell to enter the basis and jump from it to an occupied cell in its column. From there jump to another occupied cell in that row and continue in this fashion, jumping in the column, then the row, etc., until you return to the original cell. You may jump over an occupied cell in the process, but may not land on any unoccupied cell except the one for the incoming variable. A cycle or loop always exists, is unique, and has an even number of cells.

23. Move around the loop alternately labeling the cells with a + or -, starting with a + on the incoming cell. Find the cell labeled with a - that has the smallest assignment. Subtract the amount from every cell labeled with a - and add it to every cell labeled with a +. Drop the cell that goes to zero. If more than one goes to zero, drop only one, carrying the rest as zero assignments. This is necessary because there must always be exactly m+n-1 cells in the solution for MODI to work.

24. If the total amount available does not equal the total required, the problem is not balanced. An unbalanced problem can be balanced by adding an extra or dummy row (if requirements exceed availability) or column (if availability exceeds requirements). The costs in the dummy row or column are zero unless there is good reason to use some other cost. An occupied cell in a dummy row represents unfilled demands. An occupied cell in a dummy column represents shipments that are not actually made.

25. Degeneracy exists when the number of positive cells in the solution is less than m+n-1. Since the MODI technique requires that there be exactly m+n-1 cells in the basis, the positive ones are supplemented by cells that are assigned zero value and are part of the basis. Following the rules given in (8), (9), and (23) above will guarantee that there are always m+n-1 cells in the basis.

26. If in the final transportation tableau, any unused (nonbasic) cell has a zero evaluator, there is an alternate optimum solution. It can be found by treating that cell as if it had a negative evaluator, finding a loop for it and updating the tableau. The cost of this new solution will be the same as the cost of the previous solution.

27. The assignment problem can be solved using the transportation problem model, letting m = n and setting each availability and requirement equal to one. This method leads to a highly degenerate problem (m-1 of the cells will have assigned zeros) and is relatively slow. A more efficient solution procedure is the Hungarian method, based on the concept of opportunity losses.

28. The Hungarian method is a three step process:
    a. Calculate a tableau of opportunity losses;
    b. Determine whether an optimum assignment can be made;
    c. If not, revise the tableau and return to step (b).

29. The costs or payoffs from each job-person assignment or pairing are entered into a square matrix. If the problem is one of gain maximization the first step is to convert the matrix to costs. This can be done either by changing the signs of all gains or by subtracting the value in each cell from the largest value in the table, getting a table of opportunity losses.

30. The next two steps are row and column reductions. Subtract from each cell the smallest value in its row. This gives a row reduced matrix. Then subtract from each cell the smallest value in its column, giving a column reduced matrix. The zero-cost cells in the resulting matrix show where assignments can be made to give zero opportunity losses. If it is possible to make assignments to zero-cost cells in such a way that there is exactly one assignment in each row and one in each column, the problem is solved.

31. If an optimal assignment is not possible, the next step is to update the opportunity loss values. The first step in this is to draw a minimum number of lines through rows and columns to cover all zeros. This can be done by inspection or by following a procedure given by Sasieni, Yaspan and Friedman (see the Suggested Readings).
   a. Mark all rows without assignments.
   b. Mark unmarked columns with zeros in marked rows.
   c. Mark unmarked rows with assignments in marked columns.
   d. Repeat (b) and (c) until no further marking is possible.
   e. Draw lines through unmarked rows and marked columns.

32. Find the smallest value not covered by a line. Subtract it from every cell not covered by a line and add it to every cell at the intersection of two lines. Try again to make assignments to zero cost cells and, if not possible, repeat the line covering step.

SUGGESTED READINGS

A classic OR/MS text that presents a formal procedure for drawing the lines in the assignment problem is:

Sasieni, M., A. Yaspan, and L. Friedman, Operations Research - Methods and Problems, (New York: John Wiley & Sons, Inc., 1959).

Application articles include:

Eldredge, D. L. , "A Cost Minimization Model for Warehouse Distribution Systems," Interfaces, v. 12, n. 4 (August 1982), pp. 113-119.

Hansen, P. and R. E. Wendell, "A Note on Airline Commuting," Interfaces, v. 12, n. 1 (February 1982), pp. 85-87.

Markland, R. E., "Analyzing Multi-Commodity Distribution Networks Having Milling-in-Transit Features," Management Science, v. 21, n. 2 (August 1975), pp. B1405-B1416.

Perry, C. and M. Iliff, "Earthmoving on Construction Projects," Interfaces, v. 13, n. 1 (February 1983), pp. 79-84.

Srinivasan, V., "A Transshipment Model for Cash Management," Management Science, v. 20, n. 10 (June 1974), pp. 1350-1363.

KEY TERMS

Match each term with the appropriate definition below.

Terms

_____ 1. assignment problem

_____ 2. assignment tableau

_____ 3. cell

_____ 4. closed loop

_____ 5. column reduction

_____ 6. degeneracy

_____ 7. distribution problem

_____ 8. dummy destination

_____ 9. dummy source

_____ 10. heuristic

_____ 11. Hungarian method

_____ 12. modified distribution method (MODI)

_____ 13. opportunity loss

_____ 14. row and column indicators

_____ 15. row minimum method

_____ 16. row reduction

_____ 17. transportation problem

_____ 18. transportation tableau

_____ 19. unbalanced problem

_____ 20. VAM method

Definitions

A. A heuristic technique for solving transportation problems based on using the minimum cost cell in each row in succession.

B. An extra source added to an unbalanced transportation problem to "supply" the amount not available.

C. Subtracting the minimum cost in each row from all costs in that row in an assignment problem.

D. A formal procedure for solving the assignment problem based on minimizing opportunity losses.

E. Another name for the transportation problem.

F. A heuristic technique for solving transportation problems based on avoiding high cost cells later by looking at opportunity losses now.

G. A special type of LP problem that involves a one-to-one matching of tasks and responsibilities.

H. Subtracting the minimum cost in each column from all costs in that column in an assignment problem.

I. The element of a transportation or assignment tableau that corresponds to the decision variable.

J. A transportation problem in which the sum of the availabilities doesn't equal the sum of the requirements.

K. The number of positive assignments in a transportation problem is less than m+n-1.

L. In using the VAM technique, the difference between the least and second-least costs in a row or column.

M. A path through the transportation tableau consisting of the cell for the incoming variable and cells for existing variables.

N. An extra destination added to an unbalanced transportation problem to "receive" the extra availability.

O. A rectangular matrix containing the data and solution for a transportation problem.

P. A decision procedure based on rules-of-thumb or general guidelines as to how a good solution can be obtained for a particular problem type.

Q. A square matrix containing the data for an assignment problem.

R. A special type of LP problem that involves allocating the units of some product available at various sources to satisfy the demands at various destinations.

S. The solution to the dual problem for a transportation problem, used to compute Z_j for the nonbasic variables.

T. A method for checking for optimality and revising the solution to a transportation problem using row and column indicators.

SOLVED PROBLEM

An oil company has two refineries that ship to four distribution terminals. The per barrel shipping costs, refinery supply, and distribution terminal demand are shown in the transportation tableau below.

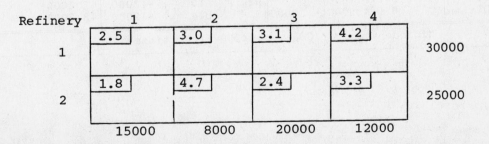

Distribution Terminal

a. Solve the problem heuristically using the row minimum heuristic.

b. Determine the optimal solution using QSB or another software package.

c. Suppose that the mode of transportation is a pipeline system. No
    pipeline exists from refinery 2 to distribution terminal 2. No pipeline
    can handle a flow of more than 15,000 barrels this week. Furthermore, an
    intermediate storage facility can be used between the refineries and the
    distribution terminals. The cost of shipping to the storage facility
    from refineries 1 and 2 is 1.10 and 1.20, respectively. The costs of
    shipping from the storage facility to the distribution terminals are 2.5,
    2.7, 2.4, and 2.9, respectively. Draw a transshipment network diagram to
    represent this version of the problem. Show all arcs, costs, supplies,
    and demands.

Solution

a. Starting in row 1, allocate 15,000 barrels to terminal 1. Moving to row
    2, allocate 20,000 barrels to terminal 3. Returning to row 1, allocate
    8,000 barrels to terminal 2. In row 2, allocate 5,000 barrels to termi-
    nal 4. Finally, allocate 7,000 from refinery 1 to terminal 4. The final
    solution has a cost of $155,400 and is shown in the tableau below.

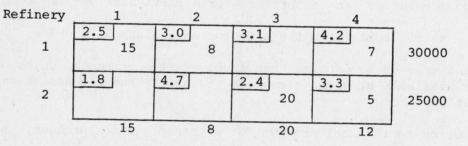

Distribution Terminal

b. QSB yields the following optimal solution. Note that cost has been
    decreased by $1,400, or 0.9 percent, relative to the row minimum solu-
    tion.

From	To	Shipment	@ cost	Opp.Ct.	From	To	Shipment	@ cost	Opp.Ct.
R1	DT1	+15000	+2.5000	0	R2	DT1	0	+1.8000	-.00000
R1	DT2	+8000.0	+3.0000	0	R2	DT2	0	+4.7000	+2.4000
R1	DT3	+7000.0	+3.1000	0	R2	DT3	+13000	+2.4000	0
R1	DT4	0	+4.2000	+.20000	R2	DT4	+12000	+3.3000	0

Summary of Results for SOLVED PROBLEM   Page : 1

Minimum value of OBJ =   154000   Iterations = 0

c. The network graph requires the addition of a transshipment node, S.

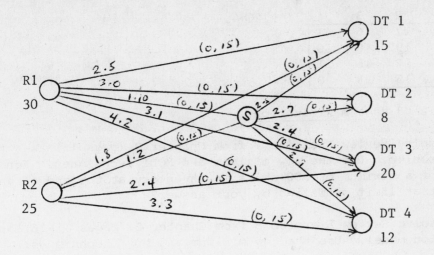

REVIEW EXERCISES
(Note: in this chapter, the symbol # denotes problems pertaining to the
supplement of Chapter 6.)

1. Given the following minimization transportation problem:

Destinations

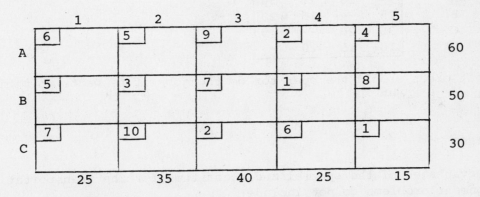

	1	2	3	4	5	
A	6	5	9	2	4	60
B	5	3	7	1	8	50
C	7	10	2	6	1	30
	25	35	40	25	15	

a. Find an initial solution using the row minimum rule.

#b. Use MODI to find the optimal solution. Do you notice anything
unusual about this problem?

c. Use VAM to find an initial solution.

#2. For the transportation tableau in Exercise 1, reverse the availabilities
of A and B (A - 50, B - 60). Find an initial solution using the row
minimum rule and use MODI to find the optimum. Do you notice anything
unusual about this problem?

#3. Solve this minimization assignment problem using the Hungarian method.

	1	2	3	4
A	23	17	6	41
B	12	19	8	30
C	9	12	15	21
D	16	5	23	8

#4 Solve Exercise 3 as a <u>maximization</u>.

#5. Set up and solve Review Exercise 7 from Chapter 2 (page 15) as a transportation problem. Use the row minimum and MODI techniques. Ignore the limitation of a maximum of 300 units in inventory at the end of any month. Is that limit satisfied by your answer?

#6. Set up and solve Review Exercise 8 from Chapter 2 (pages 15-16) as a transportation model. Use the row minimum and MODI techniques.

*#7. A machine operator has four jobs to do on his machine. The order in which he does the jobs is important because it affects the time required to convert the machine from being set up to do one job to being set up to do the next. The times required (in minutes) to convert the machine from one setup to another are given in the table.

From Job	To Job A	B	C	D
A	--	10	20	30
B	25	--	15	20
C	30	20	--	5
D	10	15	20	--

In what order should the operator do the jobs if he wants to minimize the total setup time?

CHAPTER TEST

1. The advantages of the specialized algorithms for the transportation and assignment problems do <u>not</u> include:
   a. They are much faster than using the standard simplex method.
   b. They require less computer memory.
   c. They guarantee integer solutions under all conditions.
   d. They enable larger problems to be solved.

2. Heuristic solution procedures:
   a. give optimal solutions.
   b. always give close to optimal solutions.
   c. generally work much faster than optimization procedures.
   d. can be worked without a computer.

3. In order to use the specialized algorithm for the transportation problem, you:
   a. must make the sum of the availabilities equal to the sum of the requirements.
   b. must find an initial solution using the VAM technique.
   c. must have integer cost coefficients.
   d. none of the above.

4. In using the VAM technique for finding a solution to the transportation problem:
   a. we start with an assignment to the lowest cost cell.
   b. the opportunity loss is calculated as the difference between the two lowest costs in a row or column.
   c. the opportunity cost is calculated as the difference between the lowest and highest costs in a row or column.
   d. we are guaranteed a nondegenerate solution.

5. The transportation model <u>cannot</u>, in general, be applied to:
   a. product distribution planning problems.
   b. production scheduling and inventory planning problems.
   c. assignment problems.
   d. product mix problems.

6. In using the MODI technique:
   a. the R_i and K_j values are always nonnegative.
   b. the R_i and K_j values are uniquely determined by the equation set.
   c. the sum of R_i and K_j equals C_{ij} for all basic cells.
   d. $C_{ij}-R_i-K_j \le 0$ at the optimum for minimization problems.

7. In a transshipment problem:
   a. there may be flow only out of a source.
   b. there may be flow only into a sink.
   c. there may be flow both into and out of a transshipment point.
   d. all of the above.

8. If a transportation problem is unbalanced because total supply exceeds total demand:
   a. the solution will be degenerate.
   b. we create balance by adding a dummy destination.
   c. we create balance by adding a dummy source.
   d. there will be alternate optimum solutions.

9. The most efficient method for solving the assignment problem:
   a. is the Hungarian method.
   b. can only be used on minimization problems.
   c. is a heuristic procedure.
   d. will work even if some person can do two jobs.

10. The Hungarian method:
    a. uses opportunity losses.
    b. guarantees an optimal solution.
    c. requires a square tableau.
    d. all of the above.

1. G   4. M   7. E   10. P   13. L   16. C   19. J
2. Q   5. H   8. N   11. D   14. S   17. R   20. F
3. I   6. K   9. B   12. T   15. A   18. O

Review Exercises

1.

a.

	6	5	9	2	8	
0	6 / 25	5	9 / 10 (0)	2 / 25	4 / (-4)	60
-2	5 / (1)	3 / 35	7 / 15	1 / (1)	8 / (2)	50
-7	7 / (8)	10 / (12)	2 / 15	6 / (11)	1 / 15	30
	25	35	40	25	15	

b. The initial solution found in (a) is not optimal since there is a negative evaluator in cell A5. The loop for this cell is:

        A5 - C5 - C3 - A3
        (+) (-) (+) (-)

The (-) cell with the smallest assignment is C3 with 10. Add 10 to each
(+) cell in the loop and subtract 10 from each (-) cell. The new tableau
is:

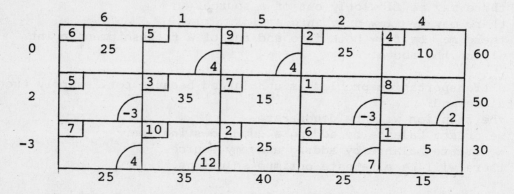

Again, this solution is not optimal. Cell B1 is the entering variable.
Its loop is:

        B1 - A1 - E1 - E3 - C3 - B3
        (+) (-) (+) (-) (+) (-)

The (-) cell with the smallest assignment is E3 with 5. Add 5 to each
(+) cell and subtract 5 from each (-) cell. The new tableau is:

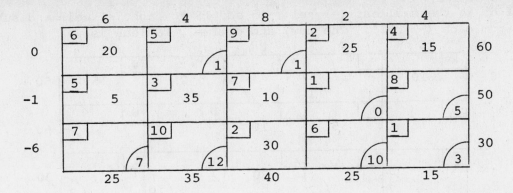

This solution is optimal since all evaluators are ≥ 0. The evaluator for
B4 is 0 which indicates that there is an alternate optimum solution,
which is:

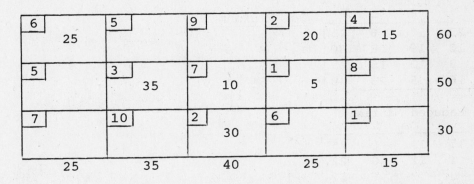

c. The initial solution found using VAM is the first optimal solution found
in (b).

2. Reversing the availabilities for A and B, the initial tableau and its row
minimum rule solution are:

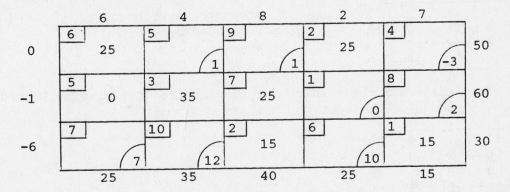

The initial solution is <u>degenerate</u>. There are only six positive assignments. A zero assignment has been entered into cell B1 to provide the
required 3+5-1 = 7 basic cells.

Cell A5 comes into the basis, using the loop:

```
A5 - C5 - C3 - B3 - B1 - A1
(+)  (-)  (+)  (-)  (+)  (-)
```

81

Cell C5 is the smallest (-) cell, so add 15 to each (+) cell and subtract 15 from each (-) cell. The new, and optimal, tableau is:

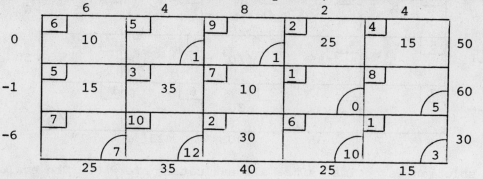

The degeneracy has disappeared. This problem also has an alternate optimal solution.

3.

23	17	6	41	Row Minimum
23	17	6	41	6
12	19	8	30	8
9	12	15	21	9
16	5	23	8	5

Row Reduced Matrix:

17	11	0	35
4	11	0	22
0	3	6	12
11	0	18	3
0	0	0	3

Column Minimum

Column Reduced Matrix:

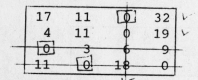

An attempted assignment is indicated by the boxes.

The check marks are the result of following the line drawing procedure given on page 73. The next tableau is:

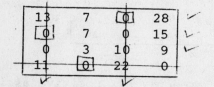

Again, this is not an optimal solution. The final tableau is:

13	4	[0]	25
[0]	4	0	12
0	[0]	10	6
14	0	25	[0]

The optimal solution is: A - 3, B - 1, C - 2, D - 4
  Its cost is 6 + 12 + 12 + 8 = 38.

82

4. In solving this as a maximization, the first step is to subtract all
    table entries from the largest cell value, 41. This gives

				Row Minimum
18	24	35	0	0
29	22	33	11	11
32	29	26	20	20
25	36	18	33	18

Row Reduced Matrix:

18	24	35	0
18	11	22	0
12	9	6	0
7	18	0	15
7	9	0	0	Column Minimum

Column Reduced Matrix:

11	15	35	[0]	✓
11	2	22	0	✓
5	[0]	6	0	
[0]	9	0	15	

9	13	23	[0]	✓
9	[0]	20	0	✓
5	0	6	2	✓
[0]	9	0	17	

4	13	18	[0]
4	[0]	15	0
[0]	0	1	2
0	14	[0]	22

This is the optimal maximizing assignment: A - 4, B - 2, C - 1, D - 3
Its value is 41 + 19 + 9 + 23 = 92.

5. Since there is both regular and overtime capacity in each month, there
    are 12 sources. Regular time availabilities are 2700 units each; over-
    time availabilities are 540 units each. The beginning inventory will be
    subtracted from the Month 1 requirements and the ending inventory will be
    added to the Month 6 requirements. Cell costs are the sum of production
    cost (assumed to be zero for regular time, since it is not given, and $5
    for overtime) and holding cost, $1 per month carried (e.g., production on
    overtime in Month 1 for use in Month 3 costs 5+2(3)=11). The matrix for
    this problem is shown on the next page. The solution shown is optimal
    and costs 2400. There are several alternate optimal solutions. The
    inventory limit is exceeded. There are 1000 units in inventory at the
    end of Months 2 and 3 and 500 at the end of Month 4.

Month

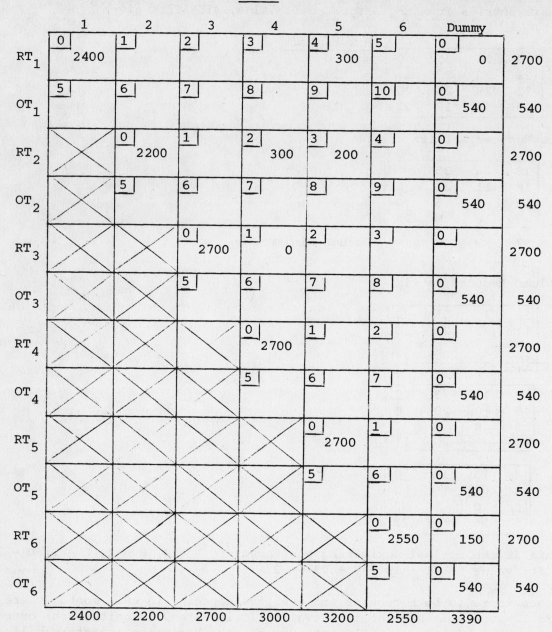

6. There are three sources - the three breweries:

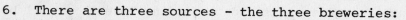

Brewery	Availability
Houston	500
Amarillo	600
San Antonio	1000
Total	2100

and three destinations - the three distribution centers:

Distribution Center	Requirements
El Paso	900
Fort Worth	600
Abilene	400
Total	1900

Since demand is less than supply, we need a dummy destination. "Shipping" costs are the sum of the production and transportation costs.

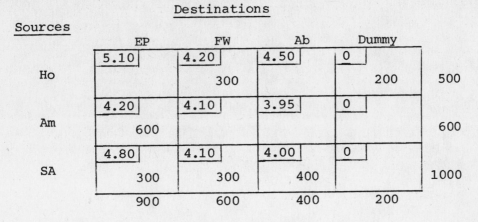

Destinations

Sources	EP	FW	Ab	Dummy	
Ho	5.10	4.20	4.50	0	500
		300		200	
Am	4.20	4.10	3.95	0	600
	600				
SA	4.80	4.10	4.00	0	1000
	300	300	400		
	900	600	400	200	

The solution shown is optimal. The cost is $8050.

7. We can approach this sequencing problem with the assignment problem, assigning a very high cost to the combinations on the main diagonal since a job cannot follow itself. If the solution does not involve a loop, it will provide an optimal sequence.

Original Matrix:

	A	B	C	D	Row Minimum
A	1000	10	20	30	10
B	25	1000	15	20	15
C	30	20	1000	5	5
D	10	15	20	1000	10

Row Reduced Matrix:

990	[0]	10	20
10	985	[0]	5
25	15	995	[0]
[0]	5	10	990

This yields an optimal solution: A - B - C - D - A

Which job the operator should do first depends on the initial setup times, doing whichever job has the shortest setup time and then following the prescribed sequence.

Chapter Test

1. c	3. a	5. d	7. d	9. a
2. c	4. b	6. c	8. b	10. d

CHAPTER SEVEN

NETWORK MODELS

MAIN POINTS

1. A <u>network</u> is a collection of <u>nodes</u> or points connected by lines or <u>arcs</u>. They arise frequently in OR/MS applications, either as an appropriate model or as a submodel within a larger model. Although network problems can be modeled and solved with LP models, their special structure leads to more efficient solution procedures. Enormous network problems with thousands or millions of variables are solved routinely in practice.

2. The transportation, transshipment, and assignment models discussed in Chapter 6 are network models. Three other types are discussed in this chapter: the shortest route problem, the minimum spanning tree problem, and the maximal flow problem.

3. In the <u>shortest route</u> problem, the objective is to find the shortest route or path along existing arcs from a designated starting node to one or more other nodes in the network. The algorithm presented finds the shortest route from the starting point to <u>all</u> other nodes.

4. The shortest route algorithm is iterative, finding at each step the shortest distance to one additional node. Thus it takes n-1 steps to find all the shortest distances for an n-node network. The algorithm has two parts. A <u>labeling</u> procedure determines the length of the shortest <u>route</u> from the starting point to each node and a <u>backtracking</u> procedure determines what that route is.

5. At the beginning of each iteration, the nodes are divided into two groups, those that are <u>permanently</u> labeled and those that are either <u>unlabeled</u> or <u>temporarily</u> labeled. A node is permanently labeled if the shortest distance from the starting point (node 1) to that node has been determined. The label consists of that distance and the immediately previous node on the route from node 1 to the node in question. Unlabeled nodes have not yet been checked. Temporarily labeled nodes are ones for which a shortest route via an already permanently labeled node has been established. Since, however, not all other nodes are permanently labeled, there is no guarantee that that temporary label (distance) will turn out, in the end, to be the shortest.

6. At each iteration, the newest addition to the permanently labeled set is used to generate new temporary labels. For each temporarily labeled or unlabeled node (call it node k) that can be reached from the newest permanently labeled node (call it j*), find the shortest distance from node 1 through node j* to node k by adding the distance to j* (part of its label) and the distance from j* to k. This total distance is compared to node k's existing temporary label distance (if it has one). If the new distance is less than the previous temporary distance, the old temporary label is replaced with a new temporary label having the new distance and j* as its two components. After this is done for all nodes k that can be

87

reached directly from j*, the temporarily labeled node with the shortest distance to node 1 is permanently labeled with that distance and the node that gives it. The process then repeats itself based on this newest permanently labeled node.

7. Backtracking simply means tracing the shortest routes back to node 1 from each node, using the second label components.

8. Applications of the shortest route model are found in equipment replacement decisions and inventory planning among other areas. The concept involved is very closely related to that used in PERT/CPM models (Chapter 8) except that there we are looking for the longest routes rather than the shortest.

9. The minimum spanning tree problem involves network design rather than the use of existing networks. A tree is a graph (a collection of arcs and nodes) with no closed loops in which the arcs provide paths along which it is possible to travel from every node to every other node. If the graph has n nodes, a tree has n-1 arcs. The minimal spanning tree problem involves selecting the arcs to form a tree which involve the minimum sum of arc lengths.

10. The minimum spanning tree algorithm is a "greedy" algorithm. In the first step any node is connected with the one closest to it by an arc. For the remaining steps, select the "free" node closest to one of those already connected by arcs, and connect it to the tree. After n-1 steps all nodes will be connected by a tree, which will have the minimum sum of arc lengths.

11. The minimum spanning tree algorithm is useful in designing networks for which the arcs do not already exist. Examples come from pipeline systems, telecommunications, and the design of road networks.

12. In the maximal flow problem, the objective is to determine the maximum amount of flow that can be moved through a network from a single designated starting point or source to a single designated ending point or sink. It is assumed that there are limits or capacities on the amount of flow along each arc in each direction.

13. One important principle in developing a solution procedure is conservation of flow: what flows into any node (other than the source and sink) must also flow out of it. The procedure used to find the maximal flow and the movements along arcs that give it is based on repeatedly finding paths from source to sink and moving maximum amounts along those paths.

14. The procedure is based on two guidelines: (a) the maximum amount that can flow along a path is determined by the smallest capacity of an arc in the path, and (b) we need to be able to revise path flows to increase the overall flow.

15. The procedure using these guidelines works with the following steps:
a. Find any path from source to sink on which movement can take place (the lowest arc capacity is greater zero).
b. Reduce the capacities on all path arcs in the direction of flow by the amount of flow on the path (the capacity of the smallest-capacity arc).

c. Increase the capacity in the reverse direction on each of those arcs by the same amount.
This last step permits future undoing of flows on certain arcs and paths to permit an increase in the overall flow from source to sink. When no further paths from source to sink can be found, the optimum has been achieved.

16. Maximal flow problems occur in studying traffic flow, pipeline systems, communication networks, and distribution systems.

SUGGESTED READINGS

Selected application articles are:

Bartholdi, J. J., et al., "A Minimal Technology Routing System for Meals on Wheels," Interfaces, v. 13, n. 3 (June 1983), pp. 1-8.

Fitzsimmons, J. A., and L. A. Allen, "A Warehouse Location Model Helps Texas Comptroller Select Out-of-State Audit Offices," Interfaces, v. 13, n. 5 (October 1983), pp. 40-46.

Glover, F., et al., "The Passenger-Mix Problem in the Scheduled Airlines," Interfaces, v. 12, n. 3 (June 1982), pp. 73-79.

Harrison, H., and D. R. Wills, "Product Assembly and Distribution Optimization in an Agribusiness Cooperative," Interfaces, v. 13, n. 2 (April 1983), pp. 1-9.

Holloran, T. J., and J. E. Byrn, "United Airlines Station Manpower Planning System," Interfaces, v. 16, n. 1 (January-February 1986), pp. 39-50.

KEY TERMS

Match each term with the appropriate definition below.

Terms

_____ 1. arc

_____ 2. arc capacity

_____ 3. backtracking

_____ 4. conservation of flow

_____ 5. label

_____ 6. maximal flow

_____ 7. minimum spanning tree

_____ 8. netform concept

_____ 9. network

_____ 10. node

_____ 11. shortest route

_____ 12. sink

_____ 13. source

_____ 14. transshipment point

_____ 15. tree

Definitions

A. In the shortest route algorithm, a pair of values giving the shortest distance to node 1 and the immediately preceding node on that path.

B. A connected series of arcs between two nodes having minimum arc length sum.

C. A node that both receives and sends out flow.

D. A line directly connecting two nodes.

E. A collection of nodes and arcs connecting them.

F. A tree with minimum total arc lengths.

G. A node that only sends out flows.

H. Identification of the network aspects of a more complex problem.

I. A point in a network, the end of an arc.

J. Tracing a path from any given node back to node 1 in the shortest route algorithm.

K. A set of arcs that makes it possible to find a path from each node to every other node in the network, containing no closed loops.

L. The maximum amount that can flow through a network with capacitated arcs.

M. A node that only absorbs flows.

N. The principle that the sum of flows into a node must equal the sum of flows out of it.

O. The maximum amount that can flow along an arc in a given direction.

SOLVED PROBLEM

Given the following pipeline network, determine the maximum flow that can pass from source to sink.

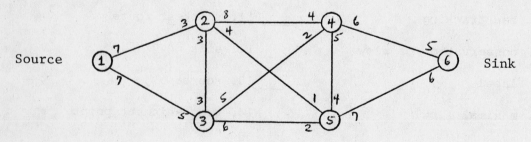

Solution

To solve the maximum flow problem, we must find a path from source to sink that is flow increase tolerant; in other words, it has the capacity for more flow along the path. Given such a path, we can ship only as much as the lowest capacity arc along the path.

1. Path 1 - 2 - 4 - 6   flow = 6
2. Path 1 - 3 - 5 - 6   flow = 6
3. Path 1 - 2 - 5 - 6   flow = 1

An alternative solution is to ship one unit along path 1-3-4-6. Since the capacity out of nodes 4 and 5 is only 13, one unit of capacity out of node 1 can not be utilized.

REVIEW EXERCISES

1. Thomas Jefferson, a college student at the University of Denver, wants to visit his girl friend in Minneapolis for spring break. In order to spend as much time as possible with her, he wants to get there as fast as possible, driving within the speed limits. The map below gives the driving time (in minutes) between cities that he could drive through. Determine Tom's fastest route. How long will the trip take?

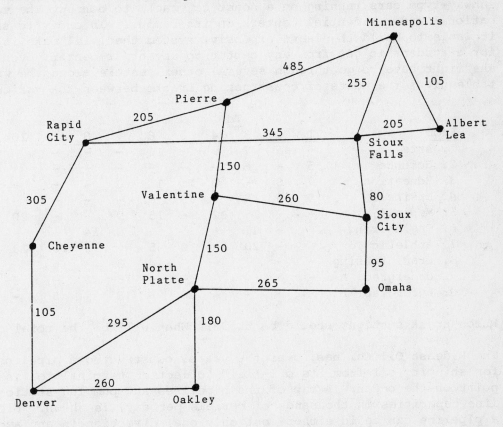

*2. The dynamic demand economic lot size problem is described as follows: At the beginning of each period there is the opportunity to place an order to cover the demands during one or more consecutive periods. If an order is placed during a period there will be a fixed ordering cost. If there is inventory on hand at the end of a period, an inventory holding cost will be incurred. Determine in which periods inventory should be purchased and in what quantities so as to minimize the total cost of meeting all demands during the planning horizon. Assume that unit purchase costs

91

are the same in all periods and that inventory will not be carried into a period in which a purchase is made.

Determine the optimal purchase and inventory plan for a six-month planning problem with the following parameter values:

Fixed purchase cost = $50
Inventory carrying cost = $1/unit/month

Month	Demand
1	10
2	20
3	5
4	15
5	12
6	8

(Hint: This problem is very similar to the equipment replacement problem.)

3. State University is planning to build a people-mover system (rubber-tired subway-type cars running on a concrete track) to connect the various educational and residential centers on its campus. In order to save costs, it wants to build the least expensive system that will make it possible for a student to get from any center to any other center, even if he or she might have to go through several other centers along the way. The table gives the costs of constructing tracks between the various centers.

From	To 1	2	3	4	5	6	7	8	9	10
1. Arts	-	5	7	9	-	16	-	-	-	-
2. Science	5	-	6	-	-	-	-	-	-	-
3. Education	7	6	-	8	15	11	20	-	-	-
4. Business	9	5	8	-	12	-	-	-	-	-
5. Medical	-	-	15	12	-	15	9	-	-	20
6. Engineering	16	-	11	-	15	-	5	14	-	-
7. Athletic	-	-	20	-	9	5	-	13	16	18
8. Grad. Housing	-	-	-	-	-	14	13	-	6	-
9. Undergrad. A	-	-	-	-	-	-	16	6	-	5
10. Undergrad. B	-	-	-	-	20	-	18	-	5	-

Which track sections should be built? What will be the total cost?

4. The Mideast Oil Co. has, over the years, constructed a pipeline system for shipping oil from its oil-field collection terminal to its shipping point on the ocean. A map of the pipelines and pumping stations, with line capacities in thousands of barrels per day, is shown. Flow through a pipeline can be in either (but only one) direction in any amount up to the capacity given.

a. Determine the maximum flow that can put through from the Field to Shipping. What quantities will move through which lines?

b. A commando group has just blown up the line connecting A and D. What will be the effect on the flow?

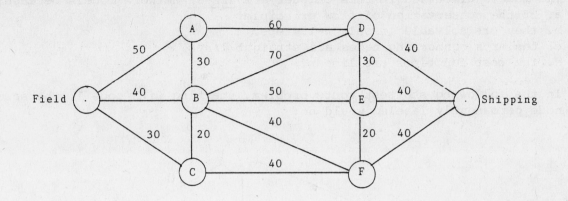

CHAPTER TEST

1. In order to become permanently labeled in the shortest route algorithm, a node must:
   a. be connected directly to node 1, the origin.
   b. be the nearest node to a permanently labeled node.
   c. have the shortest distance to node 1, the origin, of any current temporarily labeled node.
   d. be connected directly to the most recently permanently labeled node.

2. In a tree:
   a. all nodes are connected directly to all other nodes.
   b. each node can be reached from every other node by some path.
   c. every node is connected directly to the origin.
   d. there may be a closed loop connecting a set of nodes.

3. In the minimum spanning tree algorithm, the first arc selected is:
   a. the arc connecting any node with its closest neighbor.
   b. the arc connecting the two most distant nodes.
   c. the shortest arc connecting some node to the source node.
   d. the shortest arc connecting some node to the sink node.

4. The maximal flow algorithm presented in the text:
   a. allows multiple sources but only one sink.
   b. allows multiple sinks but only one source.
   c. allows only one source and one sink.
   d. allows multiple sources and multiple sinks.

5. The maximum flow along some path through the network is:
   a. the sum of the capacities of the arcs on the path.
   b. the largest capacity of an arc on the path.
   c. the smallest capacity of an arc on the path.
   d. the average of the capacities of the arcs on the path.

6. The maximum flow in a network is equal to:
   a. the capacity of the minimum cut arc set.
   b. the smallest arc.
   c. the largest arc.
   d. the sum of the smallest arc capacities in every path from the source to the sink.

7. The models discussed in this chapter are <u>linear</u> network models because:
   a. of the conservation of flow principle.
   b. they are solvable in only n-1 steps.
   c. the arcs connecting nodes are straight lines.
   d. the cost functions are linear.

8. In the following shortest route problem, starting with node 1, the second node permanently labeled would be:

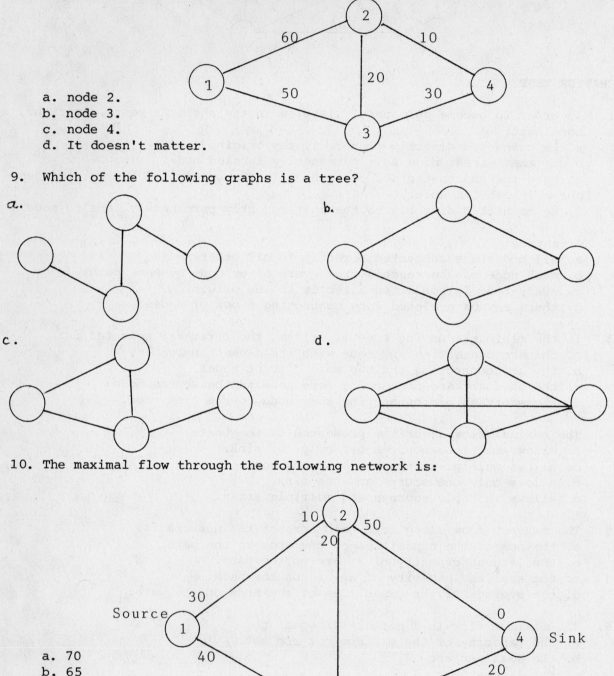

   a. node 2.
   b. node 3.
   c. node 4.
   d. It doesn't matter.

9. Which of the following graphs is a tree?

   a.

   b.

   c.

   d.

10. The maximal flow through the following network is:

   a. 70
   b. 65
   c. 45
   d. 80

94

Key Terms

1. D	4. N	7. F	10. I	13. G
2. O	5. A	8. H	11. B	14. C
3. J	6. L	9. E	10. M	15. K

Review Exercises

1. Use the shortest route through a network problem to find the minimum length (in time) route from Denver to Minneapolis.

Step	Temporary Labels	Permanent label
1	--	Denver (0)
2	Cheyenne (105, Den) N. Platte (295, Den) Oakley (260, Den)	Cheyenne (105, Den)
3	N. Platte (295, Den) Oakley (260, Den) Rapid City (410, Chey)	Oakley (260, Den)
4	N. Platte (295, Den) Rapid City (410, Chey)	N. Platte (295, Den)
5	Rapid City (410, Chey) Valentine (445, N.P.) Omaha (560, N.P.)	Rapid City (410, Chey)
6	Valentine (445, N.P.) Omaha (560, N.P.) Pierre (615, R.C.) Sioux Falls (755, R.C.)	Valentine (445, N.P.)
7	Omaha (560, N.P.) Pierre (595, Val) Sioux Falls (775, R.C.) Sioux City (705, Val)	Omaha (560, N.P.)
8	Pierre (595, Val) Sioux Falls (755, R.C.) Sioux City (655, Om)	Pierre (595, Val)
9	Sioux Falls (755, R.C.) Sioux City (655, Om) Minneapolis (1080, Pi)	Sioux City (655, Om)
10	Sioux Falls (735, S.C.) Minneapolis (1080, Pi)	Sioux Falls (735, S.C.)
11	Minneapolis (990, S.F.) Albert Lea (940, S.F.)	Albert Lea (940, S.F.)
12	Minneapolis (990, S.F.)	Minneapolis (990, S.F.)

The minimum time required to get from Denver to Minneapolis is 990 minutes or 16 hours and 30 minutes. The route to be used is: Denver, North Platte, Omaha, Sioux City, Sioux Falls, Minneapolis.

2. Following the concept of the equipment replacement decision as done using the shortest route model, we set up a <u>seven</u> node graph. The arc connecting node i with node j, i < j, represents satisfying all the demands in periods i, i+1, ..., j-1 from an order placed in period i. The length of that arc is the cost of doing this, which is the fixed cost plus the sum of the holding costs for inventory at the end of periods i, i+1, ..., j-z. Given the demand and cost figures, the arc lengths are:

Arc	Length
1-2	50
1-3	50 + 20 = 70
1-4	50 + 25 + 5 = 80
1-5	50 + 40 + 20 + 15 = 125
1-6	50 + 52 + 32 + 27 + 12 = 173
1-7	50 + 60 + 40 + 35 + 20 + 8 = 213
2-3	50
2-4	50 + 5 = 55
2-5	50 + 20 + 15 = 85
2-6	50 + 32 + 27 + 12 = 121
2-7	50 + 40 + 35 + 20 + 8 = 153
3-4	50
3-5	50 + 15 = 65
3-6	50 + 27 + 12 = 89
3-7	50 + 35 + 20 + 8 = 113
4-5	50
4-6	50 + 12 = 62
4-7	50 + 20 + 8 = 78
5-6	50
5-7	50 + 8 = 58
6-7	50

The network with these arc lengths entered is:

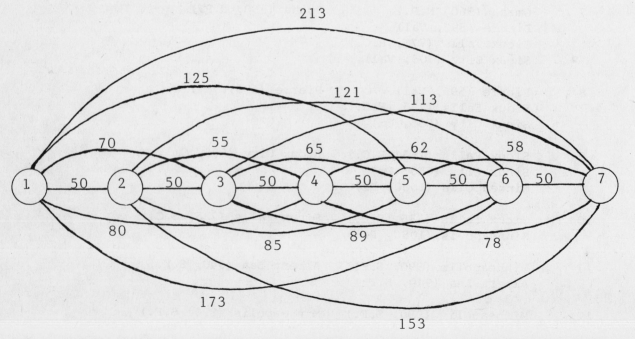

96

Following the shortest route algorithm, we get:

Step	Temporary Labels	Permanent Label
1	--	1 (0)
2	2 (50, 1)	2 (50, 1)
	3 (70, 1)	
	4 (80, 1)	
	5 (125, 1)	
	6 (173, 1)	
	7 (213, 1)	
3	3 (70, 1)	3 (70, 1)
	4 (80, 1)	
	5 (125, 1)	
	6 (171, 2)	
	7 (203, 2)	
4	4 (80, 1)	4 (80, 1)
	5 (125, 1)	
	6 (159, 3)	
	7 (183, 3)	
5	5 (125, 1)	5 (125, 1)
	6 (142, 4)	
	7 (158, 4)	
6	6 (142, 4)	6 (142, 4)
	7 (158, 4)	
7	7 (185, 4)	7 (158, 4)

The shortest path from node 1 to node 7 is the path 1-4-7 with length 158. The optimal purchasing plan is, therefore:

Buy 35 units in Month 1
Buy 35 units in Month 4

The cost of this plan is $158.

3. Use the minimal spanning tree algorithm to find the least expensive set of arcs that connect all nodes.

Step	Arc Chosen	Cost
1	Arts-Science	5
2	Science-Business	5
3	Science-Education	6
4	Education-Engineering	11
5	Engineering-Athletic	5
6	Athletic-Medical	9
7	Athletic-Grad. Hsg.	13
8	Grad. Hsg.-Undergrad. A	6
9	Undergrad. A-Undergrad. B	5
		65

The total cost is 65.

4. a. Use the maximal flow algorithm to determine the maximum amount that can flow through the network from "Field" to "Shipping." One sequence that leads to the maximal flow is:

        Field - A - D - Shipping   40
        Field - B - E - Shipping   40
        Field - C - F - Shipping   30
        Field - A - B - F - Shipping 10

The maximal flow through this network is 120.

b. Remove arc A - D and its capacity of 60. The new maximal flow can be found as:

        Field - B - E - Shipping   40
        Field - C - F - Shipping   30
        Field - A - B - D - Shipping 30

The maximal flow through this network is 100.

The new maximum flow is 100 thousand barrels per day.

Chapter Test

1. c   3. a   5. c   7. d   9. a
2. b   4. c   6. a   8. c   10. b

CHAPTER EIGHT

PROJECT SCHEDULING

MAIN POINTS

1. This chapter discusses several techniques--work breakdown structure (WBS), Gantt charts, Program Evaluation and Review Technique (PERT), and Critical Path Method (CPM)--that are useful in planning, scheduling, and controlling the timing and cost of large, complex projects.

2. These techniques are used extensively, especially by companies involved in government contracts and construction companies. The cost of using PERT or CPM on a project is not, however, insignificant. It is estimated that their use will add from one to five percent to the project's cost, but they have the potential for substantial time and cost savings.

3. A work breakdown structure (WBS) is a graphical structure or tree diagram representation of the tasks or activities involved in carrying out a specific project.

4. WBS shows the organizational structure of the project. The project is broken down into major tasks, which are further divided into tasks, then to minor tasks, and, eventually, into the smallest element in the WBS, the <u>work package</u>.

5. A work package is a detailed description of a limited portion of the project, identifying the time and resources required, the other work packages that must precede or follow it (precedence relationships), and the individual responsible for it. When all work packages have been finished, the project is complete.

6. A WBS does not provide a schedule for the project but is a preliminary, structured approach to developing the inputs necessary for a more sophisticated project scheduling technique such as PERT or CPM.

7. A Gantt chart is a horizontal bar chart that plots tasks against time. It is possible to use a Gantt chart as the basis for subjectively developing a time schedule for small, relatively simple projects. It is of more use, however, for giving a pictorial representation after a WBS has been constructed and the information used in PERT or CPM to develop a time schedule. Gantt charts are primarily used for record-keeping in monitoring projects.

8. Program Evaluation and Review Technique (PERT) and Critical Path Method (CPM) are both network techniques for planning, scheduling, and controlling large, complex projects composed of many interrelated work packages. The two techniques were developed simultaneously in the late 1950s. PERT was developed for the U. S. Navy for the Polaris submarine development project. CPM was developed for duPont for the maintenance of a chemical plant. Although somewhat different originally in terms of time determin-

ism and cost balancing efforts, the only differences now are in how the networks are drawn. The network form used here is PERT.

9. PERT comes in two basic versions, deterministic and stochastic. Deterministic PERT is useful for planning, scheduling, and controlling a project. It is used for determining the expected time to complete the project and identifying those "bottleneck" activities that have the greatest potential for delaying that completion. Stochastic PERT can be used for estimating the probability of completing the project by a specified date. Once scheduled, a project can be controlled and timing estimates updated through the continued use of PERT.

10. A PERT diagram or chart is a <u>network</u> consisting of <u>activities</u>, represented by arrows, and <u>events</u>, shown by nodes.

11. An <u>activity</u> is a task in the project, at the most detailed level a work package from WBS. In deterministic PERT, a single time estimate is made for its duration and precedence relationships showing what other activities must be completed before it is developed.

12. An <u>event</u> shows precedence relationships in the diagram. It is defined as the completion of an activity or set of activities (the predecessors) so that another activity or set of activities (the successors) can begin.

13. Features of some PERT networks are <u>dummy</u> events and/or activities. A convention in drawing PERT networks is that you may not draw two or more arrows directly between a pair of nodes, even if the activities represented by those arrows have exactly the same predecessors and successors. If there are such "twin" activities, one is represented by an arrow directly connecting two event nodes and the other is represented by an arrow going from the starting event node to a <u>dummy event</u> node showing that activity's completion, with a <u>dummy activity</u> (no real activity taking place) connecting this dummy event to the real event at the end of the other real activity.

14. A second reason for using dummy activities is overlapping predecessor sets. If two activities have some, but not all predecessors, in common, the completion of this common set is represented by an event with other events to show the completion of all activities for each successor. The subset completion event is connected by dummy activities to each complete predecessor set completion event node.

15. A <u>path</u> through a PERT network is a sequence of connected arrows and nodes showing a series of activities that follow one another.

16. The <u>longest</u> path through the network is the <u>critical path</u>. Its length determines the minimum time to complete the project. Activities on this path are <u>critical activities</u> since a delay in any of them will delay the project.

17. The scheduling of activities is based on determining for each the values for five times: early start (ES), early finish (EF), late start (LS), late finish (LF), and slack or float.

18. <u>Early start</u> and <u>finish</u> times are found by working forward through the project network, assuming the project starts on a specified date or at

time 0 and deriving the early start for each activity on the basis of the early finish times of its predecessors.

a. ES_j = the earliest time at which activity j can start assuming everything that precedes it also starts at its earliest possible time

   = maximum $\{EF_i\}$ where i precedes j

            i

b. $EF_j = ES_j + t_j$

19. The <u>late start</u> and <u>finish</u> times are found working backwards from the end of the network. Using a scheduled project completion date or, if none exists, the early project finish time as the late finish time for the ending activity or activities, the late finish time for each activity is derived from the late start times of its successors.

   a. LF_i = the latest time at which activity i can finish without delaying the project's completion

   = minimum $\{LS_j\}$ where j follows i

            j

   b. $LS_i = LF_i - t_i$

20. <u>Slack</u> or float is the flexibility in scheduling an activity. It is the amount of time by which an activity's start (or finish) can be delayed without delaying the project's completion. It is computed as the difference between an activity's late and early starts or finishes.

21. <u>Stochastic PERT</u> is used in finding the probability of completing the project by a given date if there is uncertainty as to how long activities will take.

22. Rather than using a single time estimate for the duration of each activity, three time estimates are made:

   a_i = an optimistic estimate of the time for activity i

   m_i = the most likely estimate of the time for activity i

   b_i = a pessimistic estimate of the time for activity i

23. A probability distribution is fit to these three time estimates, generally using the beta distribution because it is a continuous distribution, can be asymmetric to either side, and has a limited range.

24. The mean and standard deviation of the activity times are calculated as:

$$\overline{t}_i = (a_i + 4m_i + b_i)/6$$

$$\sigma_i = (b_i - a_i)/6$$

25. The calculation of the probability of completing the project by some specified time T is found as follows:

a. Using the expected activity times $\overline{t}_i$ in the deterministic PERT algorithm, find the <u>expected critical path</u> and its expected length T (which is the sum of the $\overline{t}_i$ for the activities on it.

b. Assuming that activity lengths are independent random variables, find the <u>variance</u> of the time to complete the expected critical path by adding the <u>variances</u> of the activities on it:

101

$\sigma_T^2 = \sum_i \sigma_i^2$ where activity i is on the expected critical path.

c. Assuming that the expected critical path consists of many activities which, in realistic problems it will, we can apply a version of the Central Limit Theorem of statistics to establish that the length of the expected critical path has an approximately Normal distribution and find the probability of completing the critical path by time t* to be:

$$P(T \le t^*) = P(Z \le [(t^* - \overline{T})/\sigma_T])$$

using the standardized Normal distribution.

26. It is noted that this probability estimation procedure can dramatically overstate the project completion probability if there are other paths through the network with expected lengths almost equal to that of the expected critical path and with large path length standard deviations. In this case, a discrete digital simulation (Monte Carlo sampling) procedure, using random numbers to sample times from the specified activity time probability distributions, can be employed to better estimate the project completion time probability distribution.

27. An enhancement of deterministic PERT (and an original feature of CPM) is the evaluation of time-cost tradeoffs.

28. For many activities it is possible, by spending additional money (added direct costs), to speed up the activity's completion time. By doing this for appropriately chosen activities, it is possible to reduce the project completion time, thereby saving costs associated with the project's length (reduced indirect or overhead costs).

29. The only activities which it makes sense to accelerate or crash are those on the critical path (or paths) since it is the length of the critical path that determines the length of the project.

30. If there is more than one critical path, the project length can be shortened only by crashing an activity that appears on all critical paths or a set of activities containing one or more from each critical path.

31. The activity(ies) to crash is(are) the one(s) with the lowest marginal crashing cost.

32. PERT/Cost is another enhancement of deterministic PERT, aimed at controlling project costs. It involves periodic review of the project to see whether actual costs are exceeding costs budgeted to that stage of the project.

33. The estimation of a project's cash flow with PERT/Cost is a five step process:
a. For each work package estimate the total cost and break it down on a period by period (usually monthly) basis.
b. Using deterministic PERT, find the critical path for the project and its associated early and late start and finish times.
c. Calculate period by period expenditures assuming all early start times.

d. Calculate period by period expenditures assuming all late start times.
e. Calculate the feasible range of period cash flows from steps (c) and (d).

34. In addition to predicting period-by-period cash needs, a PERT/Cost report can identify activities which are running over or under budget when their actual cash expenditures are compared with those projected on the basis of their percentage of completion.

35. The formulas for comparing actual and projected cash flows at a particular percentage of activity completion are:

$$V_i = \frac{P_i}{100}(B_i) \quad \text{and} \quad D_i = C_i - V_i$$

where: V_i = value of work completed for activity i

P_i = percentage of work completed for activity i

B_i = budget for activity i

C_i = actual cost to date for activity i

D_i = amount by which activity i is under or over budget to date.

36. There are many computer software packages available for project management, including versions for machines from PCs to super computers. They have widely varying capabilities, but most include most features of general interest. The availability of software has contributed significantly to the widespread use of PERT/CPM methodology.

37. Ordinary critical path analysis ignores any resource constraints that might exist. The existence of resource constraints can delay the project completion date. Resource constrained PERT analysis develops a project schedule that is feasible with respect to resource constraints. The objective is to finish the project as soon as possible while not exceeding resource limits.

38. Methods for solving resource constrained projects include optimization using integer programming and heuristics. Optimization of resource constrained projects is very limited because of the complexity of the model. The MINSLK heuristic is simple yet effective in scheduling projects.

39. The MINSLK heuristic is a priority scheduling rule in that priority is given to activities that have the least slack and are eligible (i.e., all predecessors are completed) to start. The heuristic is simple to apply, but does require the continual updating of activity slack by using the critical path calculations for ES, EF, LS, and LF.

SUGGESTED READINGS

An excellent introduction to the topics covered in this chapter and, in addition to resource leveling and several other network models, is:

Levy, J. D. and F. K. Wiest, A Management Guide to PERT/CPM, Second Edition, (Englewood Cliffs, NJ: Prentice-Hall, Inc., 1977).

Selected applications are (note the variety of the types of journals):

Bruegman, D. C., "Using Critical Path at a University," Journal of Systems Management, v. 24, n. 1 (January 1973), pp. 22-25.

Odom, R. G. and E. Blystone, "A Case Study of CPM in a Manufacturing Situation," Journal of Industrial Engineering, v. 15, n. 4 (July-August 1964), pp. 306-310.

Russell, Roberta S., and Robert T. Sumichrast, "Using PERT and Simulation to Set Promise Dates," Industrial Management, v. 31, n. 1 (January-February 1989), pp. 14-16.

Schoderbek, P. P., "PERT in College Recruiting," Management of Personnel Quarterly, v. 3, n. 4 (Winter 1965), pp. 40-43.

Wahl, R. P., Jr., "PERT Controls Budget Preparation," Public Management, v. 46 (February 1964), pp. 29-33.

Walton, H., "Experience of Application of Critical Path Method to Plant Construction," Operational Research Quarterly, v. 15, n. 1 (March 1964), pp. 9-16.

KEY TERMS

Match each term with the correct definition below.

Terms

_____ 1. activity

_____ 2. beta distribution

_____ 3. crash time

_____ 4. critical path

_____ 5. deterministic PERT

_____ 6. dummy

_____ 7. early start time

_____ 8. event

_____ 9. expected critical path

_____ 10. Gantt chart

_____ 11. late start time

_____ 12. network diagram

_____ 13. PERT

_____ 14. PERT/Cost

_____ 15. precedence relationship

_____ 16. slack time

_____ 17. stochastic PERT

_____ 18. time-cost tradeoff analysis

_____ 19. work breakdown structure

_____ 20. work package

Definitions

A. The critical path found by using expected activity times in stochastic PERT.

B. The time at which an activity could begin if all activities before it were also done as soon as possible.

C. A bar chart graph plotting tasks against time.

D. A network based approach to planning, scheduling, and controlling projects.

E. The longest path through a project network.

F. A collection of arrows and nodes used to represent a project.

G. A project planning procedure using single activity time estimates.

H. The most basic project subdivision, identifying required time and resources, precedence relationships, and the responsible individual.

I. The basic building block of a project, represented by an arrow in a PERT diagram.

J. The completion of a set of precedence activities permitting the start of follower activities.

K. The flexibility in scheduling an activity.

L. The probability distribution for activity time generally assumed in stochastic PERT.

M. The process of accelerating activities at added direct costs to reduce project time and indirect costs.

N. The reduced time in which an activity can be completed for additional cost.

O. A graph or tree diagram representing the division of a project into successively more detailed and limited task descriptions.

P. A network planning technique employing three time estimates for each activity, leading eventually to a probability distribution for project completion.

Q. Characterizes a no-time activity incorporated in a PERT diagram to show precedence.

R. The time by which an activity must begin to avoid delaying the project.

S. A variation on PERT concerned with monitoring project costs.

T. Establishes the relative order in which a pair of activities must be completed.

The information in the table below describes a project.

Activity	Immediate Predecessors	Estimated Time (weeks)
A	−	1
B	−	3
C	−	4
D	A,B	2
E	A,B	4
F	B,C	5
G	B,C	3
H	D,E,F	4
I	G	2

a. Draw a PERT network diagram for this project.

b. Find the early start, early finish, late start, late finish, and slack times for each activity.

c. Identify the critical path. What is the minimum time to complete this project?

Solution

a. The precedence relationships require the use of dummy arcs to correctly represent the project. For example, D and E both are preceded by A and B, but F and G are preceded by B and C. Thus, dummy arcs are required in front of D and E as well as F and G since neither A and B nor B and C can begin and end at the same node. The PERT diagram is shown below.

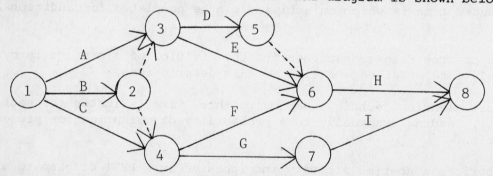

b. Using the critical path calculations, the following table is derived. Critical activities are those with no slack. Slack is calculated as LS−ES or LF−EF.

Activity	Time	ES	EF	LS	LF	Slack
A	1	0	1	4	5	4
B	3	0	3	1	4	1
C	4	0	4	0	4	0
D	2	3	5	7	9	4
E	4	3	7	5	9	2
F	5	4	9	4	9	0
G	3	4	7	8	11	4
H	4	9	13	9	13	0
I	2	7	9	11	13	4

c. The critical path is C-F-H. The project completion time is 13 weeks.

REVIEW EXERCISES

1. The information in the table describes a project.

Activity	Immediate Predecessors	Estimated Time (weeks)	Estimated Cost per week
A	–	5	$400
B	–	6	300
C	A	3	600
D	B	4	300
E	A	6	600
F	E	5	500
G	C,D	3	600

a. Draw a PERT network diagram for this project.

b. Find the early start, early finish, late start, late finish, and slack times for each activity.

c. Identify the critical path. What is the minimum time to complete this project?

d. Draw a Gantt chart for this project assuming all activities start at their early start times.

e. Develop cash flow budgets based on early and late start times.

2. In the previous exercise, suppose that each of the activities require a certain number of computer programmers. The following table indicates the number of programmers required per activity. No activity can start until all required personnel are available.

Activity	Programmers Required
A	5
B	5
C	4
D	3
E	4
F	6
G	6

a. Use the MINSLK heuristic to schedule the project with resource constraints. There are 10 programmers available.

b. What is the new project completion time and how much do the resource constraints extend the project completion time?

3. The information in the table describes a project.

Activity	Immediate Predecessors	Estimated Time (weeks) a_i	m_i	b_i
A	–	2	5	11
B	–	4	6	8
C	A	1	4	10
D	B	5	7	12
E	C,D	4	5	6
F	E	1	5	6
G	C,D	1	4	7

a. Draw the PERT network diagram for this project.

b. For each activity, find the expected value and standard deviation of its completion time.

c. Find the expected critical path.

d. Find the probability of completing the expected critical path within 25 weeks under the usual assumptions.

e. Assuming independence of path times and Normality, find the probability of completing the project within 25 weeks.

f. If you wanted to be 90 percent sure of completing the expected critical path within t weeks, what should t be?

*4. The information in the table describes a project.

Activity	Immediate Predecessors	Estimated Time (days) a_i	m_i	b_i
A	–	1	3	8
B	–	5	6	9
C	A	4	5	6
D	A	2	4	8
E	B,C	5	7	10
F	B,C	4	8	12
G	D,E,F	6	6	9
H	F	7	8	15
I	G	6	9	10
J	G,H	4	5	9
K	I,J	2	3	4

a. Draw a PERT network diagram for this project.

b. For each activity find the expected value and standard deviation.

c. Find the expected critical path.

d. Find the probability of completing the expected critical path within 40 days.

e. Find the probability that completion of the expected critical path will require at least 30 days.

f. Within how many days t can you be 95 percent sure of completing the expected critical path?

5. The information in the table describes a project.

Activity	Immediate Predecessors	Estimated Time (days) Normal	Crash	Added Cost to Crash
A	-	2	2	---
B	A	4	3	$100
C	A	5	3	150
D	B	6	4	250
E	C	7	4	300
F	D	8	5	225
G	E	4	3	90
H	F,G	4	3	110

a. Draw a PERT network diagram for this project.

b. Find the critical path using normal times.

c. Find the least expensive way to crash the project to 22 days.

d. Find the least expensive way to crash the project to the minimum time in which it can be completed.

e. If there are project-related overhead costs of $200 per day, what is the optimum length of the project? By how many days should which activities be crashed to reach this optimum?

*6. The information in the table describes a project. Times are in weeks. Note that the costs given are total costs, not incremental costs.

Activity	Immediate Predecessors	Normal Time	Cost ($)	Crash Time	Cost ($)
A	-	4	1000	3	1500
B	-	5	1200	2	1800
C	A,B	6	1800	4	2400
D	B	3	900	3	900
E	A,B	5	1000	4	1200
F	C	10	2500	8	3000
G	C,D,E	9	1800	8	2000
H	C,D,E	12	3000	9	4000
I	F,H	7	2000	5	2500
J	G	6	1800	4	2500
K	I,J	2	200	2	200
L	I,J	5	800	3	1000

a. Draw a PERT network diagram for this project.

b. Find the critical path using normal times.

c. Determine the least expensive way to reduce the project completion time to 30 weeks.

d. If there are project-related overhead costs of $400 per week, determine the optimal project length and the minimum cost method of crashing to reach it.

7. Using the information presented in the table, develop a report showing which activities are over or under budget and the status of the project relative to the budget.

Activity	Budgeted Cost	Expenditures to Date	Percent Complete
A	$ 4,000	$ 4,200	100
B	10,000	6,000	70
C	8,000	5,000	55
D	4,000	2,000	50
E	5,000	2,000	30
F	12,000	10,000	80
G	4,000	1,000	20
H	3,000	0	0
I	2,000	0	0
J	5,000	1,000	25
K	6,000	0	0

CHAPTER TEST

1. A work package involves specifying:
   a. the resources required.
   b. the responsible individual.
   c. all important predecessors.
   d. all of the above.

2. A Gantt chart:
   a. is a bar graph showing predecessor relationships.
   b. is a record-keeping technique for monitoring projects.
   c. shows project costs.
   d. none of the above.

3. In a PERT network diagram:
   a. an activity is represented by a circle.
   b. an event is based on precedence relationships.
   c. there can be only one critical path.
   d. all of the above.

4. The critical path in a PERT network diagram:
   a. is the path with the largest number of activities on it.
   b. is the shortest path through the network.
   c. is the longest path through the network.
   d. is the path with activities having maximum slack.

5. If in a deterministic PERT network diagram, an activity has an estimated duration time of 10, an early start time of 33, and a late finish time of 50, its slack time is:
   a. 17.
   b. 43.
   c. 40.
   d. 7.

110

6. For a particular activity, the three time estimates for its duration are:
   optimistic - 15, most likely - 20, pessimistic - 30
   Using the usual stochastic PERT assumptions, the expected duration is:
   a. 20.
   b. 21.67.
   c. 2.5.
   d. 20.83.

7. The variance of the time to complete the activity described in Question 6 is:
   a. 6.25.
   b. 2.5.
   c. 15.
   d. 56.25.

8. The expected critical path for a project has three activities whose duration standard deviations are 1.0, 1.5, and 0.5, respectively. The standard deviation for the path completion time is:
   a. 3.00.
   b. 3.50.
   c. 1.87.
   d. 1.00.

9. The probability distribution of the time to complete a project is always the probability distribution of the time to complete the expected critical path.
   a. True.
   b. False.

10. In evaluating time-cost tradeoffs, we start by crashing the activity on the critical path that is:
    a. the activity with the least incremental cost per time unit crashed.
    b. the activity with the least incremental cost.
    c. the activity that can be crashed the most.
    d. the longest activity.

11. PERT/Cost involves:
    a. cost estimates for each activity.
    b. predicting cash flows.
    c. identifying activities that are over budget.
    d. all of the above.

ANSWER KEY

Terms

1. I	5. G	9. A	13. D	17. P
2. L	6. Q	10. C	14. S	18. M
3. N	7. B	11. R	15. T	19. O
4. E	8. J	12. F	16. K	20. H

1.
a.

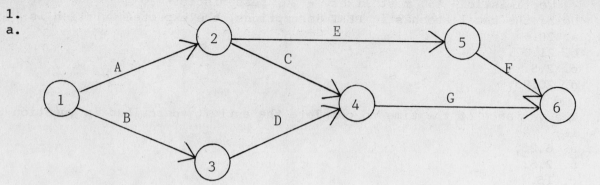

b.

Activity	Time	ES	EF	LS	LF	Slack
A	5	0	5	0	5	0
B	6	0	6	3	9	3
C	3	5	8	10	13	5
D	4	6	10	9	13	3
E	6	5	11	5	11	0
F	5	11	16	11	16	0
G	3	10	13	13	16	3

c. Critical Path: A-E-F, Project Completion Time = 16 weeks

d.

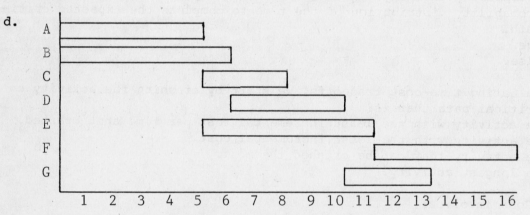

Week	Early Time Cash Budget	Late Time Cash Budget
1	130	80
2	130	80
3	130	80
4	130	130
5	130	130
6	350	150
7	375	150
8	375	150
9	175	150
10	175	175
11	300	375
12	300	375
13	300	375
14	100	300
15	100	300
16	100	300

2. At the beginning of the project, A and B are eligible to start and together require ten programmers. Since ten are available, both can be scheduled to start at time 0. When A is done, both C and E can start at time 5. However, when B is finished at time 6, D is eligible to start but cannot since three programmers are not available. Thus, D is delayed until C is completed at time 8. The complete list of scheduling decisions is shown below.

Week	Activities Eligible to start	Slack	Start Time	Finish Time
1	A	0	0	5
	B	3	0	6
6	C	5	5	8
	E	0	5	11
7	D	3	-	-
9	D	1	8	12
12	F	0	11	16
13	G	1	-	-
16	G	0	16	19

b. The new project completion time is 19 weeks which is an extension of 3 weeks beyond the unconstrained time of 16 weeks.

3.
a.

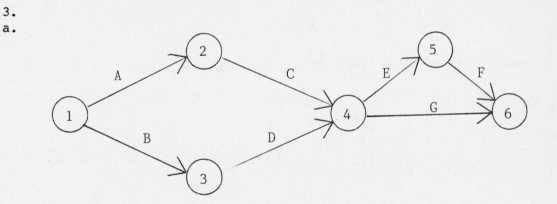

b.

Activity	a	m	b	$\bar{t}$	σ
A	2	5	11	5.5	1.50
B	4	6	8	6.0	0.67
C	1	4	10	4.5	1.50
D	5	7	12	7.5	1.17
E	4	5	6	5.0	0.33
F	1	5	6	4.5	0.83
G	1	4	7	4.0	1.00

c.

Activity	$\bar{t}$	ES	EF	LS	LF	Slack
A	5.5	0	5.5	3.5	9.0	3.5
B	6.0	0	6.0	0	6.0	0
C	4.5	5.5	10.0	9.0	13.5	3.5
D	7.5	6.0	13.5	6.0	13.5	0
E	5.0	13.5	18.5	13.5	18.5	0
F	4.5	18.5	23.0	18.5	23.0	0
G	4.0	13.5	17.5	19.0	23.0	5.5

Expected Critical Path: B-D-E-F

d. $E(\text{Path Time}) = \bar{t}_B + \bar{t}_D + \bar{t}_E + \bar{t}_F = 6.0 + 7.5 + 5.0 + 4.5 = 23.0$

$\quad = (\delta_B^2 + \delta_D^2 + \delta_E^2 + \delta_F^2)^{1/2} = (.67^2 + 1.17^2 + .33^2 + .83^2)^{1/2}$

$\quad = (2.6111)^{1/2} = 1.616$

$P(\text{Path Time} \leq 25) = P(Z \leq \dfrac{25 - 23)}{1.616} = P(Z \leq 1.24) = .8925$

e. Path A-C-E-F

$E(\text{Path Time}) = 5.5 + 4.5 + 5.0 + 4.5 = 19.5$

$\delta = (1.50^2 + 1.50^2 + .33^2 + .83^2)^{1/2} = 2.303$

$P(\text{Path Time} \leq 25) = P(Z \leq \dfrac{25 - 19.5}{2.303}) = P(Z \leq 2.39) = .9916$

Path A-C-G

$E(\text{Path Time}) = 5.5 + 4.5 + 4.0 = 14.0$

$\delta = (1.50^2 + 1.50^2 + 1 \ 0^2)^{1/2} = 2.345$

$P(\text{Path Time} \leq 25) = P(Z \leq \dfrac{25 - 14}{2.345}) = P(Z \leq 4.69) = 1.00$

Path B-D-G

$E(\text{Path Time}) = 6.0 + 7.5 + 4.0 = 17.5$

$\delta = (.67^2 + 1.17^2 + 1.0^2)^{1/2} = 1.675$

$P(\text{Path Time} \leq 25) = P(Z \leq \dfrac{25 - 17.5}{1.675}) = P(Z \leq 4.48) = 1.00$

Path B-D-E-F (Expected Critical Path)

$P(\text{Path Time} \leq 25) = .8925$ from (d)

Overall: $P(\text{All Paths} \leq 25) = (.9916)(1.0)(1.0)(.8925) = .885$

f. Z value for 90 percent probability = 1.28

$t = E(\text{Path Time}) + Z\delta = 23.0 + 1.28(1.616) = 25.07$

4.
a.

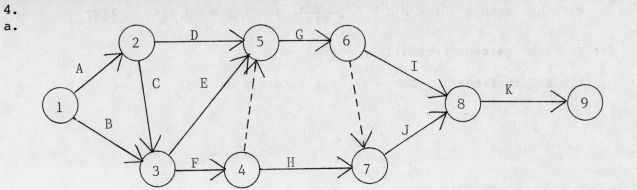

b.

Activity	a	m	b	$\bar{t}$	σ
A	1	3	8	3.50	1.17
B	5	6	9	6.33	0.67
C	4	5	6	5.00	0.33
D	2	4	8	4.33	1.00
E	5	7	10	7.17	0.83
F	4	8	12	8.00	1.33
G	6	6	9	6.50	0.50
H	7	8	15	9.00	1.33
I	6	9	10	8.67	0.67
J	4	5	9	5.50	0.83
K	2	3	4	3.00	0.33

c.

Activity	$\bar{t}$	ES	EF	LS	LF	Slack
A	3.50	0	3.50	0	3.50	0
B	6.33	0	6.33	2.17	8.50	2.17
C	5.00	3.50	8.50	3.50	8.50	0
D	4.33	3.50	7.83	12.17	16.50	8.67
E	7.17	8.50	15.67	9.33	16.50	.83
F	8.00	8.50	16.50	8.50	16.50	0
G	6.50	16.50	23.00	16.50	23.00	0
H	9.00	16.50	25.50	17.17	26.17	.67
I	8.67	23.00	31.67	23.00	31.67	0
J	5.50	25.50	31.00	26.17	31.67	.67
K	3.00	31.67	34.67	31.67	34.67	0

Expected Critical Path: A-C-F-Dummy-G-I-K

d. $E(\text{Path Length}) = \bar{t}_A + \bar{t}_C + \bar{t}_F + \bar{t}_G + \bar{t}_I + \bar{t}_K$

$$= 3.5 + 5.0 + 8.0 + 6.5 + 8.67 + 3.0 = 34.67$$

$$\sigma = (\sigma_A^2 + \sigma_C^2 + \sigma_F^2 + \sigma_G^2 + \sigma_I^2 + \sigma_K^2)^{1/2}$$

$$= (1.17^2 + .33^2 + 1.33^2 + .50^2 + .67^2 + 33^2)^{1/2}$$

$$= (4.0556)^2 = 2.014$$

$$P(\text{Path Length} \leq 40) = P(Z \leq \frac{40 - 34.67}{2.014}) = P(Z \leq 2.65) = .996$$

115

e. $P(\text{Path Length} \geq 30) = P(Z \geq \dfrac{30 - 34.67}{2.014}) = P(Z \geq -2.32) = .9898$

f.   Z for 95 percent probability = 1.64

   $t = E(\text{Path Length}) + Z\sigma = 34.67 + 1.64(2.014) = 37.97$ days

5.
a.

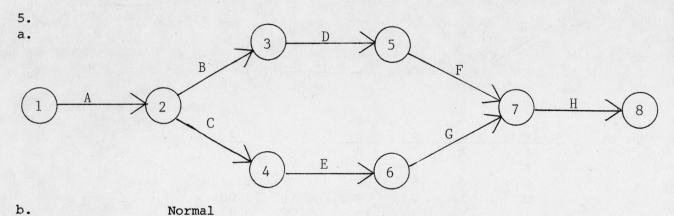

b.

Activity	Normal Time	ES	EF	LS	LF	Slack
A	2	0	2	0	2	0
B	4	2	6	2	6	0
C	5	2	7	4	9	2
D	6	6	12	6	12	0
E	7	7	14	9	16	2
F	8	12	20	12	20	0
G	4	14	18	16	20	2
H	4	20	24	20	24	0

Critical Path: A-B-D-F-H

c.

Time	Activity to Crash	Cost to Crash
24	-	--
23	F	75
22	F	75

Crash F by 2 days at a cost of $150

d.   Continuing the table in (c), at this point the other path, A-C-E-G-H, is also critical.

Time	Activity to Crash	Cost to Crash	Notes
21	H	110	
20	F,C	150	F used up
19	B,C	165	B,C used up
18	D,G	215	G used up
17	D,E	225	D used up

e.   Optimum length is 19 days. Up to that point, crashing costs less per day than the $200 saved. For days 18 and 17, the cost of crashing exceeds the savings of $200 per day.

6.

a.

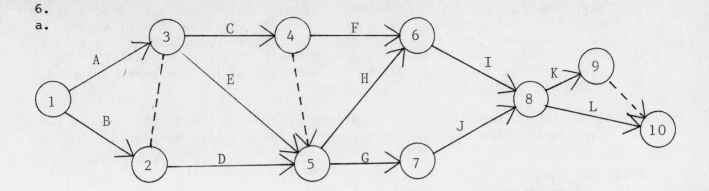

b.

	Normal						For part (c) Marginal
Activity	Time	ES	EF	LS	LF	Slack	Crash Cost
A	4	0	4	1	5	1	500
B	5	0	5	0	5	0	200
C	6	5	11	5	11	0	300
D	3	5	8	8	11	3	-
E	5	5	10	6	11	1	200
F	10	11	21	13	23	2	250
G	9	11	20	15	24	4	200
H	12	11	23	11	23	0	333
I	7	23	30	23	30	0	250
J	6	20	26	24	30	4	350
K	2	30	32	33	35	3	-
L	5	30	35	30	35	0	100

Critical Path: B-C-Dummy-H-I-L

c. The first step is to find the <u>marginal</u> cost per week of crashing activities by dividing the difference between Crash and Normal Costs by the
difference between Crash and Normal Times.   These values have been
included in the table in (b) in the right-hand column.

Time	Activity to Crash	Cost to Crash	Notes
35	-	-	
34	L	100	
33	L	100	L used up
32	B	200	A becomes critical
31	I	250	
30	I	250	I used up

Crash L by 2 weeks at a cost of $200, B by 1 week at a cost of $200 and I
by 2 weeks at a cost of $500.   The total crashing cost is $900.

d. Continue with the table in (c) until we reach the point at which the Cost
to Crash exceeds $400.

Time	Activity to Crash	Cost to Crash	Notes
29	C	300	E becomes critical
28	H	333	
27	H	333	F,G,J become critical

To reduce the time any further would require reducing a set of activities at a total cost exceeding $400. The optimal length is thus 27 weeks. The way to reach it is to crash those activities specified in (c) plus C by 1 week at a cost of $300 and H by 2 weeks at a cost of $666.67. The total crashing cost is $900 from (c) and $966.67 for the added crashing, a total of $1866.67.

7. The relevant consideration is that the percent of budget that should have been spent is the same as the percent of the activity completed.

Activity	Budgeted Cost	Percent Complete	Forecasted Expenditures	Expenditures to Date	Over (Under) Budget
A	4,000	100	4,000	4,200	200
B	10,000	70	7,000	6,000	(1000)
C	8,000	55	4,400	5,000	600
D	4,000	50	2,000	2,000	–
E	5,000	30	1,500	2,000	500
F	12,000	80	9,600	10,000	400
G	4,000	20	800	1,000	200
H	3,000	0	0	0	–
I	2,000	0	0	0	–
J	5,000	25	1,250	1,000	(250)
K	6,000	0	0	0	–
Total	63,000	48.5	30,550	31,200	650

At this point the project is approximately 48.5 percent complete (30,550/63,000). It is $650 over budget. Activities A, C, E, F, and G are all over budget. Activities B and J are under budget. Activity D is right on its budget. Activities H, I, and K have not yet started.

Chapter Test

1. d	3. b	5. d	7. a	9. b	11. d
2. b	4. c	6. d	8. c	10. a	

CHAPTER NINE

INTEGER AND GOAL PROGRAMMING

MAIN POINTS

1. Many decision problems violate the linear programming assumptions of divisibility or a single objective to be optimized. For these problems the techniques of integer programming, goal programming, or multiple objective LP may prove useful.

2. Integer programming (IP) is important for two primary reasons. First, many real problems require whole-number solutions. Second, using variables restricted to being either 0 or 1 permits modeling structural issues that cannot be addressed with LP.

3. Pure- or all-integer models require all variables to have integer values. Mixed-integer models require some integer variables. 0-1 models limit all variables to being either 0 or 1. The model type has implications for the solution procedure.

4. IP solution procedures are much less efficient in general than LP solution. They require more computer storage and time. Thus, in general, they are limited to smaller problems than LP, although special structure may permit solving very large IP problems.

5. The primary methods for solving IP problems are: (1) LP with rounding, (2) complete enumeration, (3) cutting-planes, and (4) partial enumeration by branch and bound.

6. Rounding off LP solutions is easy but may lead to non-optimal or infeasible solutions. Complete enumeration of all possible solutions is generally infeasible.

7. Cutting-plane techniques involve adding additional constraints to each successive solution to the problem to eliminate the previous non-integer corner solution without eliminating any feasible integer solutions. They tend to be slow and have the added disadvantage of not giving any integer solution until the optimum is found.

8. Branch and bound methods are most popular. After solving the LP relaxation of the problem (the same problem without the integer requirement), we have an integer solution or some fractional variables. In the latter, two new problems are created (branching) by adding constraints to the previous problem that restrict a fractional variable to being $\leq$ the integer less than the fraction (Problem 1) and $\geq$ the integer greater than the fraction (Problem 2).

9. For each new feasible problem without an integer solution, a bound is established by solving it as an LP or by some other method. The bound causes the problem to be discarded (bound is worse than best current

integer solution) or a candidate for further branching. To stop branching is called <u>fathoming</u>.

10. 0-1 IP models have found use in several areas. Capital budgeting problems involve allocating limited investment budgets among alternative projects. Set covering problems involve covering or providing for a set of conditions at minimum cost. Examples are facility location, crew scheduling, vehicle routing, and assembly line balancing.

11. 0-1 variables can be used within what would otherwise be regular LP or IP problems to model some non-linear characteristics. Examples are fixed charges, multiple-choice constraints, k-out-of-n alternatives constraints, and if-then constraints.

12. LP and IP both involve problems with a single objective to be optimized. In any problems there are multiple objectives, which may be incompatible or conflicting.

13. Solving such problems involves evaluating tradeoffs among performance levels on the various objectives. A useful concept here is non-dominance of solution. A solution is nondominated if it has a better value than all other possible solutions on at least one objective. There is no absolute optimal solution unless there is only one nondominated solution. A decision maker can, however, choose among nondominated solutions to "best" meet the multiple objectives.

14. Searching all nondominated solutions for the most satisfactory overall is generally not feasible. Three primary approaches to searching a reasonable number of alternatives are goal programming, multiple objective LP, and interactive computer-based methods.

15. The best developed and most popular of these approaches is goal programming (GP), which may be either nonpreemptive and weighted or preemptive. The nonpreemptive approach assumes the goals are comparable and differ by numerical weights. In the preemptive method, the goals are ranked in priority order.

16. Preemptive GP attempts to achieve or get as close as possible to every specified goal level, a concept called <u>satisficing</u>. Achievement of goals is addressed in priority order, first achieving or satisfying as best as is possible the highest priority goal. Each successive priority level goal is then addressed, attempting to satisfy it without reducing the satisfaction level on any higher priority goal.

17. GP differs from regular LP or IP in that the goal expressions are built in as constraints. Each goal constraint includes a pair of <u>deviational variables</u> that measure the amount by which the goal is under- or over-satisfied. Regular structural LP constraints may also be included. The GP objective function is a prioritized linear function of the deviational variables. The objective is to minimize the deviations from the goals.

18. Besides recognizing multiple objectives, a further advantage of GP over LP is that constraint requirements are allowed to be "soft." That is, if a constraint that cannot technically be met is expressed as a goal, the result will be an unsatisfied goal rather than an infeasible LP problem.

19. A disadvantage of GP as a multiple objective LP methodology is that it may lead to dominated solutions. This follows from the a priori specification of goal levels and priorities.

20. The solution procedure for preemptive GP is a modification of the LP simplex method. There is a C_j-Z_j row for each priority level. The problem is solved in stages, optimizing with respect to each C_j-Z_j row in turn, being careful not to violate the optimality achieved for higher priority levels.

21. Multiple objective linear programming (MOLP) differs from GP in that each objective is expressed individually as a linear function to be optimized. Thus, we have a regular LP with more than one explicit objective function. There are no goals or deviational variables.

22. A complete solution involves finding all nondominated solutions, linear combinations of the individual solutions for each objective function, and choosing from among them subjectively. In practice, this is difficult.

23. The primary approaches to MOLP include: (1) multicriterion simplex method, finding all (or many) nondominated solutions, (2) objective function weighting, using a weighted combination of the objective functions, and (3) interactive approaches, which involve choices from successive solution sets in order to develop new solution alternatives. No single approach is recognized as best.

24. Computer packages are available for all methodologies discussed. However, they are generally less successful than those for LP. Special codes for problems with special structure, such as facility location or set covering problems, are available and more efficient.

SUGGESTED READINGS

Selected applications are:

Integer Programming

Abara, J., "Applying Integer Linear Programming to the Fleet Assignment Problem," Interfaces, v. 19, n. 4 (July-August 1989), pp. 20-28.

Bell, W. J., et al., "Improving the Distribution of Industrial Gases with an On-line Computerized Routing and Scheduling Optimizer," Interfaces, v. 13, n. 6 (December 1983), pp. 4-23.

Patel, N. R., "Locating Rural Social Service Centers in India," Management Science, v. 25, n. 1 (January 1979), pp. 22-30.

Woolsey, R. E. D., "A Candle to St. Jude, or Four Real World Applications of Integer Programming," Interfaces, v. 2, n. 2 (February 1972), pp. 20-27.

Goal Programming

Bammi, D. and D. Bammi, "Development of a Comprehensive Land Use Plan by Means of a Multiple Objective Mathematical Programming Model," *Interfaces*, v. 9, n. 2, Part 2 (April 1979), pp. 50-63.

Kendall, K. E. and S. M. Lee, "Formulating Blood Rotation Policies with Multiple Objectives," *Management Science*, v. 26, n. 11 (November 1980), pp. 1145-1157.

Lee, S. M. and M. J. Schniederjans, "A Multicriteria Assignment Problem: A Goal Programming Approach," *Interfaces*, v. 13, n. 4 (August 1983), pp. 75-81.

Multiple Objective Linear Programming

Christman, J. J., et al., "A Multiobjective Linear Programming Methodology for Public Sector Tax Planning," *Interfaces*, v. 19, n. 5 (September-October 1989), pp. 13-22.

KEY TERMS

Match each term with the appropriate definition below.

Terms

_____ 1. bounding

_____ 2. branching

_____ 3. cutting plane

_____ 4. deviational variables

_____ 5. fathomed

_____ 6. goal programming

_____ 7. integer programming

_____ 8. LP relaxation

_____ 9. multiple objective LP

_____ 10. nondominated solution

_____ 11. objective function weighting

_____ 12. partial enumeration

_____ 13. preemptive

_____ 14. satisficing

Definitions

A. Making decisions to achieve specified goal levels rather than to optimize.

B. Creating new LP problems by adding constraints based on integerizing a fractional solution variable.

C. Combining multiple objective functions by multiplying them by fractional weights and adding them to create a single objective function.

D. Recognition that a branch-and-bound subproblem node should not be used for further branching due to infeasibility, integer solution, or an inferior bound.

E. Solving goal programming problems recognizing goals in priority order.

F. LP problems in which a solution is to be developed by trading off among the optimization of several objectives simultaneously.

G. A constraint added to an integer programming problem to eliminate a fractional solution without eliminating any integer solutions.

H. A variation on LP in which some or all of the variables are required to have integer values.

I. A variation on LP in which multiple objectives are addressed by establishing goal levels and attempting to satisfy them.

J. The LP version of an integer programming problem in which the integer requirement has been dropped.

K. Establishing a limit on the value of the objective function for a subproblem in a problem solution tree.

L. A solution to a multiple objective problem which is better than all other feasible solutions on at least one objective.

M. A variable which measures the amount by which a goal is under- or over-achieved.

N. A solution approach which explicitly tests only some of the feasible solutions, rejecting the rest by implication of nonoptimality.

SOLVED PROBLEM

For the following integer programming problem, graph the solution space, identifying all feasible solutions, and determine which is best.

$$\text{maximize} \quad 6X_1 + 4X_2$$
$$\text{subject to:} \quad 5X_1 + 3X_2 \leq 17$$
$$2X_1 + 4X_2 \leq 11$$
$$X_2 \leq 2$$
$$X_1, \ X_2 \geq 0 \text{ and integer}$$

Solution

The graphical solution of IP problems is similar to that of LP problems. One main difference, however, is that there is no procedure like the simplex method that successively provides an improved solution at each iteration and converges rapidly to the optimal solution.

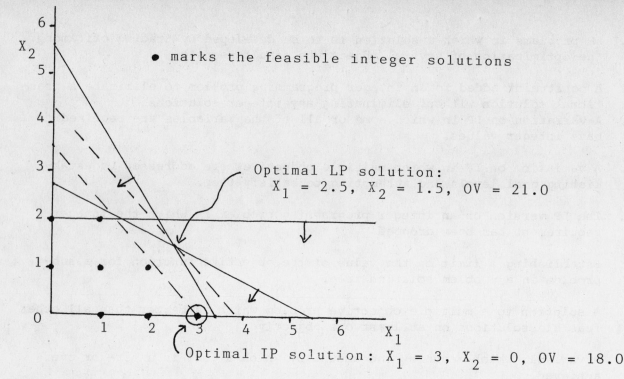

marks the feasible integer solutions

Optimal LP solution:
$X_1 = 2.5$, $X_2 = 1.5$, OV = 21.0

Optimal IP solution: $X_1 = 3$, $X_2 = 0$, OV = 18.0

Thus, in graphing the feasible region and the feasible lattice points, we could resort to trial and error to find the optimal solution. Another approach is to determine the LP optimum and search lattice points that are in the feasible region and "close" to the optimal LP extreme point. However, examples exist in which lattice points that are "far" from the LP optimum are the integer optimum. In the graph, note that $X_1 = 2.5$ and $X_2 = 1.5$ is the optimal LP solution. There are nine feasible lattice points. Trying (1,2), (2,1), and (3,0), we find that $X_1 = 3$ and $X_2 = 0$ yields an objective function value of 18 and is the optimal integer solution.

REVIEW EXERCISES

1. The Wealthy Investment Co. has to decide how to invest its present and projected available capital. There are a number of investment opportunities available, each of which has certain capital requirements over the next three periods. The information about capital requirements and net present values for the potential projects is given in the table.

	Capital Requirements			
Project	Per. 1	Per. 2	Per. 3	Net Present Value
1	5	6	2	27
2	3	4	4	22
3	8	-1*	-1*	14
4	4	-4*	-4*	18
Capital Available	12	11	8	

*a negative value means a cash inflow

Develop a 0-1 integer programming model to maximize the total net present value of the projects selected while not violating the capital availability in any period (capital cannot be carried over from period to period) and meeting the following additional constraints:

a. Projects 1 and 2 are incompatible; you cannot invest in both.

b. Investing in Project 4 is conditional on having invested in Project 1.

2. For the solved problem, solve by partial enumeration using branch and bound.

3. The MoGo Company produces three types of electric-powered vehicles: golf carts, security vehicles, and in-house delivery trucks. The resources required to produce one unit of each vehicle are given in the table on the next page.

Resources	Vehicle Type			Available
	Golf	Security	Delivery	
Wheels	3	4	6	200
Seats	2	2	1	75
Batteries	1	1	2	50
Labor (hrs.)	6	7	8	250
Revenue	$800	$1000	$1500	

Develop a goal programming model that recognizes the following goals in priority order as given:

Priority	Goal
1	Achieve $40,000 in revenue.
2	Minimize the overtime worked.
3	Produce at least 50 vehicles.

4. Use the graphical approach to solve the goal programming problem below.

$$\text{minimize} \quad P_1 d_1^+ + P_2(d_2^+ + d_2^-) + P_3 d_3^-$$

$$\text{subject to:} \quad X_1 + 2X_2 \leq 10$$

$$X_1 + 4X_2 + d_1^- - d_1^+ = 12$$

$$2X_1 + X_2 + d_2^- - d_2^+ = 4$$

$$.5X_1 + X_2 + d_3^- - d_3^+ = 4$$

$$X_1, X_2, \text{ all d's} \geq 0$$

5. For the following multiple objective linear programming problem, find the set of nondominated solutions.

$$\text{maximize} \quad X_1 + 3X_2$$

$$\text{maximize} \quad 3X_1 + X_2$$

$$\text{subject to:} \quad 2X_1 + X_2 \leq 8$$

$$2X_1 + 3X_2 \leq 15$$

$$X_1 \leq 3$$

$$X_2 \leq 4$$

$$X_1, X_2 \geq 0$$

*6. The Good-Profits Medical Corporation is planning an expansion of its walk-in medical facilities into a metropolitan area. They have to decide how many facilities to open and where they should be located, recognizing that a potential user of such centers will be less likely to use it, the farther away from his or her home that it is. For planning purposes the metropolitan area has been divided into six districts. Preliminary site analyses have been conducted. On this basis, four potential sites have been located. On each site, it would be possible to build either a large or small facility. Information on facility sizes and costs and on the planning districts is given in the tables below.

Facility Size	Fixed Cost	Annual Cost	Annual Capacity
Large	$1,000,000	$360,000	40,000
Small	700,000	200,000	20,000

		Distance to Location			
District	Population	A	B	C	D
1	100,000	1	6	3	4
2	120,000	2	4	3	5
3	140,000	5	1	2	4
4	120,000	7	3	2	3
5	160,000	5	5	3	1
6	100,000	3	7	4	2

It is assumed that an ideally located facility would draw .20 annual visits per area resident. Ten percent of this potential is assumed to be lost for each mile of distance. For example, the potential number of visits from District 1 is .2(100,000) = 20,000. A facility 3 miles away (at C) would lose 30 percent of that potential, leaving 14,000 visits.

Combine the ideas of 0-1 variables and goal programming to develop a model for deciding on site locations and sizes that addresses the following goals:

Priority	Goal
1	Develop at least 100,000 total visits per year.
2	Keep total fixed costs to $2.5 million.
3	Restrict annual operating costs to $900,000.
4	Open no more than three facilities

CHAPTER TEST

1. In an integer programming problem, it is required:
   a. all parameter values be integer.
   b. some or all decision variable values be integer.
   c. the objective function value be an integer.
   d. the slack and/or surplus variables be integer.

2. Solving an integer programming problem by LP round-off gives a solution that:
   a. may not be optimal.
   b. may not be feasible.
   c. may not be close to optimal.
   d. all of the above.

3. The generally most efficient optimization technique for integer programming problems is:
    a. LP round-off.
    b. complete enumeration.
    c. partial enumeration by branch and bound.
    d. cutting-plane.

4. In the branch and bound approach to integer programming, a node is fathomed if:
    a. its bound is better than the value of an existing solution.
    b. it gives a feasible integer solution.
    c. the computer runs out of storage space.
    d. it branches into subproblems.

5. A cutting plane in integer programming:
    a. eliminates an integer solution.
    b. divides the problem into subproblems.
    c. eliminates a fractional solution.
    d. immediately generates an integer solution.

6. Partial enumeration techniques:
    a. evaluate part of the answer.
    b. eliminate a part of the variable set.
    c. only use some of the coefficients.
    d. implicitly reject part of the solution space.

7. 0-1 variables cannot be used to model:
    a. fixed charges.
    b. mutually exclusive variables.
    c. the product of variables.
    d. choosing a subset of alternatives.

8. Goal programming problems:
    a. evaluate only nondominated solutions.
    b. are solved just like LP problems.
    c. require setting goal levels.
    d. all of the above.

9. A deviational variable:
    a. may be negative.
    b. must appear in the GP objective function.
    c. must be less than the goal level.
    d. measures deviation from a goal.

10. In order to use preemptive goal programming, the decision maker must:
    a. set goal levels on all goals.
    b. establish priorities for the goals.
    c. be able to express the goals as linear expressions.
    d. all of the above.

11. If a goal calls for not exceeding a limit, the objective function would include:
    a. its positive deviation variable.
    b. its negative deviation variable.
    c. both of its deviation variables.
    d. neither of its deviation variables.

127

12. Multiple objective LP:
   a. is restricted to maximization problems.
   b. only permits two objectives.
   c. requires weighting the objectives.
   d. none of the above.

ANSWER KEY

<u>Terms</u>

1. K	4. M	7. H	10. L	13. E
2. B	5. D	8. J	11. C	14. A
3. G	6. I	9. F	12. N	

<u>Review Exercises</u>

1. The problem is to determine which projects to invest it.

Define: $X_i = \begin{cases} 1 \text{ if they invest in Project i} \\ 0 \text{ if not} \end{cases}$

maximize $\quad 27X_1 + 22X_2 + 14X_3 + 18X_4$

subject to:
$$5X_1 + 3X_2 + 8X_3 + 4X_4 \leq 12 \quad \text{Period 1}$$
$$6X_1 + 4X_2 - 1X_3 - 4X_4 \leq 11 \quad \text{Period 2}$$
$$2X_1 + 4X_2 - 1X_3 - 4X_4 \leq 8 \quad \text{Period 3}$$
$$X_1 + X_2 \leq 1 \quad \text{(a)}$$
$$-X_1 + X_4 \leq 0 \quad \text{(b)}$$
$$X_1, X_2, X_3, X_4 = 0 \text{ or } 1$$

2. First solve the problem as a regular LP. If the solution is not integer, branch on a non-integer variable to create two new problems and solve them. Continue in this fashion until all derived problems have been fathomed. A tree diagram showing the development of the problems is shown on the next page.

3. The problem is to determine how many vehicles of each type to produce.

Define: G, S, D as the numbers of golf, security, and delivery vehicles to produce

minimize $\quad P_1(d_1^-) + P_2(d_2^+) + P_3(d_3^-)$
subject to:
   Structural constraints:

$$3G + 4S + 6D \leq 200 \quad \text{Wheels}$$
$$2G + 2S + D \leq 75 \quad \text{Seats}$$
$$G + S + 2D \leq 50 \quad \text{Batteries}$$

128

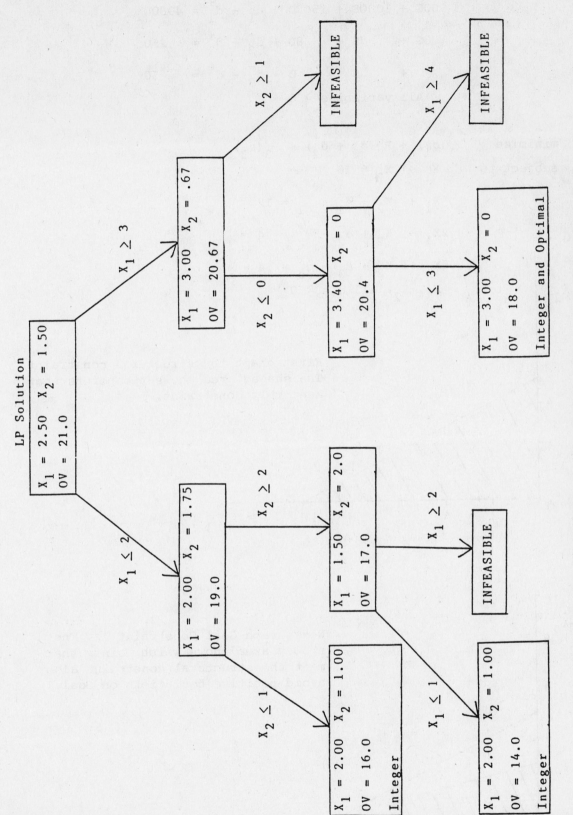

Tree diagram for branch-and-bound solution of Problem 2.

129

Goal constraints:

$$800G + 1000S + 1500D + d_1^- - d_1^+ = 40000$$

$$6G + \quad 7S + \quad 8D + d_2^- - d_2^+ = \quad 250$$

$$G + \quad S + \quad D + d_3^- - d_3^+ = \quad 50$$

All variables ≥ 0

5.

minimize $\quad P_1^+(d_1^+) + P_2(d_2^- + d_2^+) + P_3(d_3^-)$

subject to $\quad X_1 + 2X_2 \leq 10$

$$X_1 + 4X_2 + d_1^- - d_1^+ = 12$$

$$2X_1 + X_2 + d_2^- - d_2^+ = 4$$

$$.5X_1 + X_2 + d_3^- - d_3^+ = 4$$

$$X_1,\ X_2,\ \text{all d's} \geq 0$$

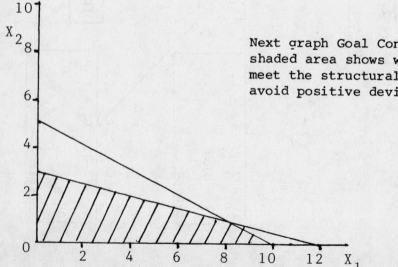

First graph the structural constraint. The shaded area shows the points that meet that constraint.

Next graph Goal Constraint 1. The shaded area shows which points that meet the structural constraint also avoid positive deviations on Goal 1.

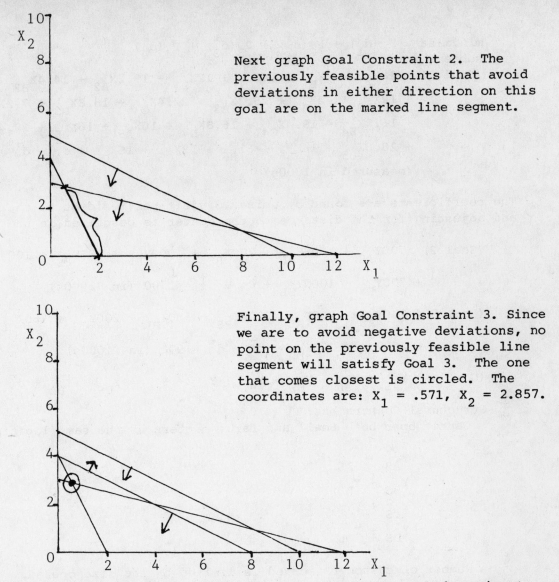

Next graph Goal Constraint 2. The previously feasible points that avoid deviations in either direction on this goal are on the marked line segment.

Finally, graph Goal Constraint 3. Since we are to avoid negative deviations, no point on the previously feasible line segment will satisfy Goal 3. The one that comes closest is circled. The coordinates are: $X_1 = .571$, $X_2 = 2.857$.

6. The problem is to determine where to locate facilities and what size to use. We must also plan on how much of the potential demand from each district to plan to satisfy at each facility.

Define: $Y_{iS} = \begin{cases} 1 \text{ if a small center is built at location i} \\ 0 \text{ if not} \end{cases}$

$Y_{iL} = \begin{cases} 1 \text{ if a large center is built at location i} \\ 0 \text{ if not} \end{cases}$

X_{ij} = fraction of demand from district j that is planned to be served at center i

131

minimize $P_1(d_1^-) + P_2(d_2^+) + P_3(d_3^+) + P_4(d_4^+)$
subject to:

(Goal 1) $18X_{A1} + 8X_{B1} + 14X_{C1} + 12X_{D1} + 19.2X_{A2} + 14.4X_{B2} + 16.8X_{C2}$

$+ 12X_{D2} + 14X_{A3} + 25.2X_{B3} + 22.4X_{C3} + 16.8X_{D3} + 7.2X_{A4}$

$+ 16.8X_{B4} + 19.2X_{C4} + 16.8X_{D4} + 16X_{A5} + 16X_{B5} + 22.4X_{C5}$

$+ 28.8X_{D5} + 14X_{A6} + 61_{B6} + 12X_{C6} + 16X_{D6} + d_1^- - d_1^+ = 100$

(measured in 1000s)

The coefficients are found by using .2 visit per resident of the district and adjusting for the distance to the center as described in the problem.

(Goal 2) $700Y_{AS} + 1000Y_{AL} + 700Y_{BS} + 1000Y_{BL} + 700Y_{CS} + 1000Y_{CL}$

$+ 700Y_{DS} + 1000Y_{DL} + d_2^- - d_2^+ = 2500$ (in \$1000s)

(Goal 3) $200Y_{AS} + 360Y_{AL} + 200Y_{BS} + 360Y_{BL} + 200Y_{CS} + 360Y_{CL}$

$+ 200Y_{DS} + 360Y_{DL} + d_3^- - d_3^+ = 900$ (in \$1000s)

(Goal 4) $Y_{AS} + Y_{AL} + Y_{BS} + Y_{BL} + Y_{CS} + Y_{CL} + Y_{DS} + Y_{DL} + d_4^- - d_4^+ = 3$

Structural Constraints:
Cannot open both Small and Large centers at the same location.

$$Y_{AS} + Y_{AL} \leq 1$$
$$Y_{BS} + Y_{BL} \leq 1$$
$$Y_{CS} + Y_{CL} \leq 1$$
$$Y_{DS} + Y_{DL} \leq 1$$

Number of customers served is limited by the size opened.

$18X_{A1} + 19.2X_{A2} + 14X_{A3} + 7.2X_{A4} + 16XA_5 + 14X_{A6}$
$- 20Y_{AS} - 40Y_{AL} \leq 0$ (measured in 1000s)

$8X_{B1} + 14.4X_{B2} + 25.2X_{B3} + 16.8X_{B4} + 16X_{B5} + 6X_{B6}$
$- 20Y_{BS} - 40Y_{BL} \leq 0$

$14X_{C1} + 16.8X_{C2} + 22.4X_{C3} + 19.2X_{C4} + 22.4X_{C5} + 12X_{C6}$
$- 20Y_{CS} - 40Y_{CL} \leq 0$

$12X_{D1} + 12X_{D2} + 16.8X_{D3} + 16.8X_{D4} + 28.8X_{D5} + 16X_{D6}$
$- 20Y_{DS} - 40Y_{DL} \leq 0$

Cannot satisfy more than 100 percent of demand.

$$X_{A1} + X_{B1} + X_{C1} + X_{D1} \leq 1$$
$$X_{A2} + X_{B2} + X_{C2} + X_{D2} \leq 1$$
$$X_{A3} + X_{B3} + X_{C3} + X_{D3} \leq 1$$
$$X_{A4} + X_{B4} + X_{C4} + X_{D4} \leq 1$$
$$X_{A5} + X_{B5} + X_{C5} + X_{D5} \leq 1$$
$$X_{A6} + X_{B6} + X_{C6} + X_{D6} \leq 1$$

All variables ≥ 0, all Y's = 0 or 1

Chapter Test

1. b	3. c	5. c	7. c	9. d	11. a
2. d	4. b	6. d	8. d	10. d	12. d

CHAPTER TEN

DYNAMIC PROGRAMMING

MAIN POINTS

1. While linear, integer, and goal programming are most used for single-period or static decision problems, dynamic programming (DP), as its name implies, is best suited for multiperiod or multistage decision problems in which a sequence of interacting decisions is required and problem parameters may change over time.

2. Applications of DP include production and distribution problems, inventory control, scheduling, resource allocation, employment decisions, replacement and maintenance decisions, and product standardization decisions.

3. DP might more appropriately be called serial or recursive optimization since it works by breaking the problem down into smaller subproblems, called stages, which are solved sequentially, tying the stages together through recursive relationships.

4. A major conceptual difference between DP and the other mathematical programming and network models discussed in earlier chapters is that DP is not a specific technique but is a solution approach or philosophy. Like the branch and bound method, discussed in Chapter 9 in the context of integer programming but applicable to a number of other kinds of problems, DP requires a tailor-made or custom designed model and solution process for each application. There are, however, similarities among the models. It is these general concepts that are the focus here.

5. In formulating a DP model for a specific application it is necessary to keep in mind the following concepts and terminology: stage, state, policy decision, return, and recursive relationship.

6. Each problem is broken down into stages, which are points in time or some other natural division of the problem where decisions are to be made. The number of stages may be finite, as in the problems discussed in this text, or infinite, meaning that it is a recurring problem for which a solution policy is to be developed.

7. When a decision is to be made at a particular stage the system will be in one of a number of states or conditions. The states are used to describe the status of the system at the time of the decision. State space descriptions may be either finite or infinite and, if infinite, may be either discrete (usually integer) or continuous. Continuous problems are generally addressed with calculus.

8. A policy is a decision rule or set of decisions which tells, for every stage and state, what the decision is or how it is to be made. The effect of the decision is to transform the system from being in its present state at its current stage to being in some state at the next

stage. In a deterministic DP problem, as is discussed in this text, this next state will be completely determined by the present state and the decision. In a probabilistic DP problem, the next state will be determined according to a probability distribution that recognized the current state and decision.

9. The result of applying a particular decision rule to a particular stage and state is a <u>return</u> or net payoff, which may be either a gain or cost. This is analogous to the LP objective function, except that it looks only at the present stage and state and the state transformed to rather than looking at the overall return.

10. The <u>recursive relationship</u> is a mathematical statement that ties the stages together. It specifies that the total return or value of being in the present stage and state and making a decision is a combination of the immediate return from moving to the next stage and the total return associated with all stages after this one.

11. The key concept in modeling and solving DP models is the <u>Principle of Optimality</u>, which states that regardless of how a particular state is arrived at in a given stage, the decisions made after that must constitute an optimal policy for the rest of the stages (i.e., what happened before this point is irrelevant). What is important is the present situation and the best that can be done starting from here.

12. The stages in DP are generally counted back from the end. Thus, stage n means that there are n stages left.

13. Defining:

    n = decision variable at stage n

    s_n = state variable at stage n

    $r_n(s_n, x_n)$ = return at stage n from making decision x_n when in state s_n

    the general form of the DP recursion for an additive return function is:

    $$f_n(s_n, x_n) = r_n(s_n, x_n) + f_{n-1}^*(s_{n-1}, x_{n-1})$$

    That is, the cost of making decision x_n when in state s_n, n stages from the end, is equal to the immediate return from making that decision in that stage and state plus the optimal return for all future stages (of which there are n-1), given that we would then be in state s_{n-1}. The decision that would be made under those conditions, $x_n^*(s_n)$, is the one that would optimize $f_n(s_n, x_n)$ and give $f_n^*(s_n, x^*)$.

14. The primary advantages of DP are:
    a. for some problems it is the only technique that will give an optimal solution;
    b. it is well-suited for multistage, multiperiod, or sequential decision processes;
    c. it is broad in scope, applicable to a wide variety of problem characteristics;
    d. it is readily adapted to the computer and can provide some sensitivity analysis.

15. The primary disadvantages are:
    a. there is no general formulation for DP so each problem must be modeled uniquely;
    b. the "curse of dimensionality" that implies large numbers of state variables lead to excessive storage and computational requirements;
    c. it is not particularly efficient for problems where an alternative math programming model can be used.

SUGGESTED READINGS

Selected application articles are:

Alstrup, J., et al., "Booking Control Increases Profit at Scandinavian Airlines," Interfaces, v. 19, n. 4 (July-August 1989), pp. 10-19.

Davis, S. G. and E. T. Reutzel, "A Dynamic Programming Approach to Work Force Scheduling with Time-Dependent Performance Measures," Journal of Operations Management, v. 1, n. 3 (February 1981), pp. 165-171.

Hay , D. A. and P. N. Dahl, "Strategic and Midterm Planning of Forest-to-Product Flows," Interfaces, v. 14, n. 5 (October 1984), pp. 33-43.

Sarin, S. C. and W. E. Benni, "Determination of Optimal Pumping Policy of a Municipal Water Plant," Interfaces, v. 12, n. 2 (April 1982), pp. 43-48.

Schrage, L. and K. R. Baker, "Dynamic Programming Solution of Sequencing Problems with Precedence Constraints," Operations Research, v. 26, n. 3 (June 1978), pp. 444-449.

KEY TERMS

Match each term with the appropriate definition below.

Terms

_____ 1. curse of dimensionality   _____ 5. return

_____ 2. policy decision   _____ 6. stage

_____ 3. principle of optimality   _____ 7. state

_____ 4. recursive relationship

Definitions

A. The mathematical expression that links the returns and decisions of the various stages of the problem.

B. The condition in which a system is at a stage.

C. The more state variable possibilities there are, the greater the amount of computation and storage required for solution.

D. The payoff or value of making a particular decision when in a given stage and state.

E. No matter how we got to where we are, the future decisions must be optimal for our present position.

F. An opportunity to make a decision.

G. The set of decisions or rule for making decisions depending on the state one is in.

SOLVED PROBLEM

The sales manager for a sporting goods manufacturer is trying to decide how many sales personnel to assign to each territory. The total expected sales volumes for each territory with various numbers of sales personnel assigned to it are shown in the table.

| Territory | 0 | Number of Sales People | | | | |
		1	2	3	4	5
East	0	100	180	255	315	360
Central	0	110	200	270	330	380
West	0	90	180	260	320	370

How many sales people should be assigned to each territory if there are five total people available? Assume fractional assignments are not possible.

Solution

In any dynamic programming formulation, it is necessary to identify the stages, states, and return function. This problem breaks naturally into 3 stages where each stage is represented by a territory. The order is not important, but let East be stage 1; Central, stage 2; and West, stage 3. The state of the system is defined by the number of salespersons available for assignment. In the last stage, we know we have 5 available. In stages 1 and 2, the states can range from 0 to 5, depending on how many were used in the succeeding stage. The return function is based on the total sales volume for the territory under consideration as a function of the number of salespersons available.

Stage 1: East

$$f_1(s_1) = \max_{x_1} (r_1(s_1, x_1))$$

| State | Decision Possibilities | | | | | | x_1^* | $f_1^*(s_1)$ |
	0	1	2	3	4	5		
0	0	-	-	-	-	-	0	0
1	0	100	-	-	-	-	1	100
2	0	100	180	-	-	-	2	180
3	0	100	180	255	-	-	3	255
4	0	100	180	255	315	-	4	315
5	0	100	180	255	315	360	5	360

138

<u>Stage 2:</u> Central

$$f_2(s_2) = \max_{x_2} (r_2(s_2,x_2) + f_1^*(s_2-x_2))$$

Decision Possibilities

State	0	1	2	3	4	5	x_2^*	$f_2^*(s_2)$
0	0+0	–	–	–	–	–	0	0
1	0+100	110+0	–	–	–	–	1	110
2	0+180	110+100	200+0	–	–	–	1	210
3	0+255	110+180	200+100	270+0	–	–	2	300
4	0+315	110+255	200+180	270+100	330+0	–	2	380
5	0+360	110+315	200+255	270+180	330+100	380+0	2	455

<u>Stage 3:</u> West

$$f_3(s_3) = \max_{x_3} (r_3(s_3,x_3) + f_2^*(s_3-x_3))$$

Decision Possibilities

State	0	1	2	3	4	5	x_3^*	$f_3^*(s_3)$
5	0+455	90+380	180+300	260+210	320+110	370+0	2	480

The optimal policy is to assign:

Territory	Sales People	Sales
West	2	180
Central	2	200
East	1	100

for a total sales volume of 480.

REVIEW EXERCISES

1. Trans-Island Shipping is preparing to load a ship with goods for transport to another island. Since the total amount of material to be moved exceeds the capacity of the ship, Trans-Island can be selective in what it chooses to load. The items available are shown in the table.

Item	Units	Weight/unit	Profit/unit
1	4	20	100
2	5	30	125
3	3	40	150

The total weight capacity of the ship is 130. Use dynamic programming to determine how the ship should be loaded if only integer numbers of units can be used.

2. A manufacturer is designing a new product which has three components arranged in series, as shown in the diagram. Each component is subject to failure according to the probabilities in the table.

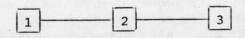

Component	Probability of Failure	Cost/unit
1	.10	20
2	.15	15
3	.05	25

For the product to work, all three components must function. The reliability of a component can be increased by putting in parallel units of the same type. As long as one of the parallel units of each type functions, the product will work. The manufacturer wants to spend no more than $100 on the components. Given the cost of each component as in the table, how many components of each type should be used? (Hint: Given the structure of the product, the probability that it will work is the product of the probabilities that each component subsystem functions. Those probabilities are each found as 1 - P(all fail).)

*3. Solve Review Exercise 2 from Chapter 7, the dynamic demand economic lot size problem, using dynamic programming. (Note: The best way of modeling this involves a somewhat different type of recursive relationship. Think of the shortest route model version of the problem.)

CHAPTER TEST

1. Dynamic programming:
   a. is only used on problems dealing with decisions over time.
   b. explicitly considers all possible sequences of decisions.
   c. can only be used with discrete variables.
   d. none of the above.

2. The concept of dynamic programming that ties the decisions at various stages together is the:
   a. state variable.
   b. stage.
   c. recursive relationship.
   d. return function.

3. The curse of dimensionality in dynamic programming refers to:
   a. states.
   b. stages.
   c. return functions.
   d. recursive relationships.

4. The principle of optimality states, in essence, that:
   a. all dynamic programming problems have optimal solutions.
   b. if there is an optimal solution, dynamic programming will find it.
   c. the best way to find optimal solutions is sequentially.
   d. the optimal solution for a given stage and state doesn't depend on how that stage and state were reached.

5. In solving a knapsack-type problem such as the capital budgeting problem in the text, the state characteristic is:
   a. the number of alternatives (projects) yet to be considered.
   b. the amount of capacity (money) yet to be allocated.
   c. the gain available from an alternative.
   d. the total gain from all alternatives considered so far.

140

6. In the problem of Question 5, the <u>stage</u> characteristic is:
   a. the number of the project to be considered.
   b. the amount of capacity (money) yet to be allocated.
   c. the gain available from an alternative.
   d. the total gain from all alternatives considered so far.

7. In the problem of Question 5, the <u>return</u> characteristic is:
   a. the number of alternatives (projects) yet to be considered.
   b. the amount of capacity (money) yet to be allocated.
   c. the gain available from an alternative.
   d. the total gain from all alternatives considered so far.

8. In the problem of Question 5, the <u>recursive relationship</u> is based on:
   a. the number of alternatives (projects) yet to be considered.
   b. the amount of capacity (money) yet to be allocated.
   c. the gain available from an alternative.
   d. the total gain from all alternatives considered so far.

9. Dynamic programming is a solution approach rather than a solution technique because:
   a. it only leads to approximately optimal solutions.
   b. each problem has to be modeled individually.
   c. not all problems can be solved with DP.
   d. computer programs don't exist for solving DP problems.

10. Which of the following is <u>not</u> relevant in a stage transformation function?
    a. the stage.
    b. the state.
    c. the decision.
    d. the return.

ANSWER KEY

Terms

1. C   3. E   5. D   7. B
2. G   4. A   6. F

Review Exercises

1. This a knapsack-type problem. The problem is:

$$\text{maximize} \quad 100X_1 + 125X_2 + 150X_3$$
$$\text{subject to:} \quad 20X_1 + 30X_2 + 40X_3 \leq 130$$
$$X_1 \leq 4$$
$$X_2 \leq 5$$
$$X_3 \leq 3$$
$$X_1, X_2, X_3 \geq 0 \text{ and integer}$$

To use dynamic programming, we define:

141

```
stage = item number
state = remaining weight capacity in boat
return = profit times units loaded
```

Stage 1: Item 1 $\qquad f_1^*(s_1) = \max_{X_1} (100X_1)$

Decision

State		X_1	X_1^*	$f_1^*(s_1)$
0 = s1	20	0	0	0
20 = s1	40	1	1	100
40 = s1	60	2	2	200
60 = s1	80	3	3	300
80 = s1 = 130		4*	4	400

*maximum units available of Item 1

Stage 2: Item 2 $\qquad f_2^*(s_2) = \max_{X_2} (125X_2 + f_1^*(130-30X_2))$

Decision Possibilities

State		0	1	2	3	4	X_2^*	$f_2^*(s_2)$
0 = s2	20	0+0	−	−	−	−	0	0
20 = s2	30	0+100	−	−	−	−	0	100
30 = s2	40	0+100	125+0	−	−	−	1	125
40 = s2	50	0+200	125+0	−	−	−	0	200
50 = s2	60	0+200	125+100	−	−	−	1	225
60 = s2	70	0+300	125+100	250+0	−	−	0	300
70 = s2	80	0+300	125+200	250+0	−	−	1	325
80 = s2	90	0+400	125+200	250+100	−	−	0	400
90 = s2	100	0+400	125+300	250+100	375+0	−	1	425
100 = s2	110	0+400	125+300	250+200	375+0	−	2	550
110 = s2	120	0+400	125+400	250+200	375+100	−	1	525
120 = s2 = 130		0+400	125+400	250+300	375+100	500+0	2	550

Stage 3: Item 3 $\qquad f_3^*(s_3) = \max_{X_3} (150X_3 + f_2^*(130-40X_3))$

Decision Possibilities

State	0	1	2	3	X_3^*	$f_3^*(s_3)$
130	0+550	150+425	300+225	450+0	1	575

The optimal policy is:

Item	Units	Value	Weight
3	1	150	40
2	1	125	30
1	3	300	60

2. This problem is also of the knapsack variety, but the returns are multiplicative, rather than additive. The probability that all of the

142

parallel units of a given type fail and that that portion of the series is broken is:

$$(p_i)^{X_i}$$

where p_i is the probability of failure of a unit of type i and X_i is the number of such units. Thus the probability that at least one of the set of type i units works is:

$$1 - (p_i)^{X_i}$$

and the probability that all three component sets each has one working is:

$$[1 - (p_1)^{X_1}][1 - (p_2)^{X_2}][(1 - (p_3)^{X_3}]$$

The problem is, therefore, to select values for X_1, X_2, and X_3 that will:

maximize $\qquad [1 - (.1)^{X_1}][1 - (.15)^{X_2}][1 - (.05)^{X_3}]$

subject to: $\qquad 20X_1 + 15X_2 + 25X_3 \leq 100$

$\qquad\qquad\quad X_1, X_2, X_3 \geq 1$ and integer

Subtracting the cost of one unit for each component (since we must have at least one of each type in the system), we revise the problem to:

maximize $\qquad [1 - (.1)^{X_1+1}][1 - (.15)^{X_2+1}][1 - (.05)^{X_3+1}]$

subject to: $\qquad 20X_1 + 15X_2 + 25X_3 \leq 40$

$\qquad\qquad\quad X_1, X_2, X_3 \geq 0$ and integer

where the X's are now the extra or parallel units of the three types. We define the stage as the component number and the state as the money left to spend.

Stage 1: Component 1 $\qquad f_1^*(s_1) = \max_{X_1} (1 - (.1)^{X_1+1})$

| | Decision | | |
State	X_1	X_1^*	$f_1^*(s_1)$
$0 \leq s_1 < 20$	0	0	.90
$20 \leq s_1 < 40$	1	1	.99
$s_1 = 40$	2	2	.999

Stage 2: Component 2 $\quad f_2^*(s_2) = \max\,[(1 - (.15)^{X_2+1})f_1^*(40-15X_2)]$

Possible Decisions

State	0	1	2	X_2^*	$f_2^*(s_2)$
$0 \leqslant s_2 < 15$	(.85)(.9)	–	–	0	.765
$15 \leqslant s_2 < 20$	(.85)(.9)	(.9775)(.9)	–	1	.87975
$20 \leqslant s_2 < 30$	(.85)(.99)	(.9775)(.9)	–	1	.87995
$30 \leqslant s_2 < 35$	(.85)(.99)	(.9775)(.9)	(.996625)(.9)	2	.8969625
$35 \leqslant s_2 < 40$	(.85)(.99)	(.9775)(.99)	(.996625)(.9)	1	.967725
$s_2 = 40$	(.85)(.999)	(.9775)(.99)	(.996625)(.9)	1	.967725

Stage 3: Component 3 $\quad f_3^*(s_3) = \max\,[(1 - .05^{X_3+1})f_2^*(40-25X_3)]$

Possible Decisions

State	0	1	X_3^*	$f_3^*(s_3)$
$s_3 = 40$	(.95)(.967725)	(.97725)(.87995)	0	.91934

The optimal strategy is to use:

Component	Added Number	Total Number	Cost	Probability of Working
3	0	1	25	.95
2	1	2	30	.9775
1	1	2	40	.99

The total cost is \$95 and the probability that the product works is .91934.

4. Repeating the information from the original description of the problem on page 91:

Fixed purchase cost = \$50
Inventory carrying cost = \$1/unit/month

Month*	Demand
6	10
5	20
4	5
3	15
2	12
1	8

*The month numbers have been reversed to count back from the end.

We define the stage number as the period or month number. Based on the assumption that inventory will not be carried into a period in which an order will be placed, we do not need to keep track of inventory (as in the Purchasing-Inventory example in the text, since the inventory at the time of any purchase will be zero. This also implies that whenever a purchase is made it will cover the exact requirements for some specific number of periods, beginning with the period of purchase. Thus we will use as our state variable the number of periods left in the planning horizon for which purchases need to be made.

The concept of the recursive relationship is handled somewhat differently in this problem than in the other problems. Since the stage variable is the number of the period in the problem and a decision to purchase may cover more than one period, eliminating the need for a purchase for the next period, two, three, etc., we may be skipping stages, moving from a purchase in period n to one in period n-2, n-3, etc. This idea leads to the recursive relationship:

$$f^*_n(n) = \min_i [c(n,i) + f^*_{n-i}(n-i)]$$

where $c(n,i)$ is the cost of purchasing in period n to cover the demands for i periods. This cost is composed, as were the arc lengths in the solution to Exercise 2 in Chapter 7, of the fixed purchase cost in period n plus the inventory carrying costs in periods n, n-1, n-2, ..., n-i+1 until the next purchase in period n-i. Since the state and stage are the same, we will drop the stage subscript and simply use:

$$f^*(n) = \min_i [c(n,i) + f^*(n-i)]$$

$f^*(0)$ will be equal to zero.

Month 1:   If a purchase must be made in the last period, there is no choice as to the amount, it covers the last period only, so $f^*(1) = 50$

Month 2: $f^*(2) = \min_i [c(2,i) + f^*(2-i)]$

i	c(2,i)	c(2,i) + f*(2-i)	Optimal Decision	f*(2)
1	50+0	50+50		
2	50+8	58+0	2	58

Month 3: $f^*(3) = \min_i [c(3,i) + f^*(3-i)]$

i	c(3,i)	c(3,i) + f*(3-i)	Optimal Decision	f*(3)
1	50+0	50+58		
2	50+12	62+50		
3	50+20+8	78+0	3	78

Month 4: $f^*(4) = \min_i [c(4,i) + f^*(4-i)]$

i	c(4,i)	c(4,i) + f*(4-i)	Optimal Decision	f*(4)
1	50+0	50+78		
2	50+15	65+58		
3	50+27+12	89+50		
4	50+35+20+8	113+0	4	113

Month 5: $f^*(5) = \min\limits_{i} [c(5,i) + f^*(5-i)]$

i	c(5,i)	c(5,i) + f*(5-i)	Optimal Decision	f*(5)
1	50+0	50+113		
2	50+5	55+78	2	133
3	50+20+15	85+58		
4	50+32+27+12	121+50		
5	50+40+35+12+8	145+0		

Month 6: $f^*(6) = \min\limits_{i} [c(6,i) + f^*(6-i)]$

i	c(6,i)	c(6,i) + f*(6-i)	Optimal Decision	f*(6)
1	50+0	50+133		
2	50+20	70+113		
3	50+25+5	80+78	3	158
4	50+40+20+15	125+58		
5	50+52+32+27+12	173+50		
6	50+60+40+35+20+8	213+0		

Examining the results for Month 6, we see that the first purchase should cover 3 months, making the next decision necessary in Month 3 (from the end). That order should also cover 3 months, so there should be purchases in the third and sixth periods from the end, or in the original Months 1 and 4. The Month 1 purchase is for 35 units (original Months 1, 2, and 3) and the Month 4 purchase is for 35 units (original Months 4, 5, and 6). The total cost is 158.

Chapter Test

1. d	3. a	5. b	7. c	9. b
2. c	4. d	6. a	8. d	10. d

CHAPTER ELEVEN

PROBABILITY CONCEPTS AND DISTRIBUTIONS

MAIN POINTS

1. Probability is a way of expressing the likelihood or chance that some event will occur. Since most real-world decisions are made under conditions that are neither totally certain nor uncertain, the use of probability theory for organizing relevant information about likelihoods can lead to better decisions.

2. Probabilities are either <u>objective</u> or <u>subjective</u>. Objective probabilities are based on historical information or rigorous analysis to support the values used. Subjective probabilities are based on the personal experience and intuition of the decision maker, although there is often a base of partially relevant information.

3. The specific outcome of a random phenomenon or occurrence is an <u>event</u>, which may be either <u>simple</u> or <u>compound</u>. A simple event is a single, narrowly defined outcome of the phenomenon, such as the pair of values on a roll of a pair of dice or the sequence of heads and tails in flipping a coin several times. A compound event is a set of simple events that satisfy some broader criterion of interest, such as the pair of dice results in a sum of seven or there are two heads in three flips of a coin.

4. In assessing or assigning probabilities for a particular random phenomenon or <u>experiment</u>, we need to specify the <u>universe</u> or set of all possible outcomes in simple event terms. Such simple outcomes are called <u>sample points</u> and the set of all possible sample points for the experiment is called the <u>sample space</u>.

5. To be used as probabilities for a particular experiment, the values assigned to represent the likelihoods of various events must satisfy certain rules or axioms:
   a. <u>Nonnegativity</u>: The probability of any event E is between 0 and 1: $0 \leq P(E) \leq 1$.
   b. <u>Additivity</u>: If two events E and F in the sample space have no points in common, the probability of one or the other occurring is their sum: $P(E \text{ or } F) = P(E) + P(F)$.
   c. <u>Completeness</u>: If S is the entire sample space, its probability is 1: $P(S) = 1$.

6. The completeness and additivity axioms lead to the concept of <u>complementarity</u> and its probability. Two events are complementary if the second consists of all sample points that are not in the first. The complement of E is designated by $\overline{E}$ and $P(\overline{E}) = 1 - P(E)$.

7. The additivity property refers to events that are <u>mutually exclusive</u>, meaning that they have no sample points in common. Rolling a seven and rolling an eleven on a pair of dice are mutually exclusive since a single roll of the dice cannot give both results. A set of events is called <u>collectively exhaustive</u> if, among them, they contain all sample points

for the experiment. Complementary events are both mutually exclusive (no overlap in membership) and collectively exhaustive (any point not in one is in the other).

8. When we describe the outcome of a probability experiment in terms of more than one event, we can refer to probabilities as being joint, marginal, or conditional.

9. A joint probability refers to the outcome of the phenomenon being simultaneously included in two events (i.e., the probability the outcome is in E and F). For example, a single roll of a die may result in a value that is odd and less than four.

10. The probability associated with only one of these events, ignoring whether it is or is not also the other, is called a marginal probability, since if the probabilities are displayed in a two-way classification table representing the two events of interest, the marginal probabilities are found by summing across rows or down columns and writing the row and column sums in the margins of the table.

11. If the knowledge that the outcome is in one event is used to adjust the probability of being in another event, the probability of this second event is conditional on the knowledge of the first. The probability, $P(A|B)$, read "A given B," is found as:

$$P(A|B) = \frac{P(A \text{ and } B)}{P(B)} \quad \text{if } P(B) \neq 0.$$

Conditional probabilities are extremely useful because they permit the decision maker to revise the assessed likelihood of an outcome of interest based on related information.

12. Two rules for combining probabilities that make it possible to compute the probabilities of more complex combinations of events are the additive and multiplicative laws.

13. The additive law is a generalization of the additive property that allows for the possibility that the two events of interest may not be mutually exclusive:

$$P(A \text{ or } B) = P(A) + P(B) - P(A \text{ and } B).$$

The subtraction step eliminates the double counting of the probabilities of simple events that appear in both A and B.

14. The multiplicative law is a rearrangement of the conditional probability function that permits the calculation in certain cases of the joint probability of A and B:

$$P(A \text{ and } B) = P(A)P(B|A) = P(B)P(A|B).$$

15. Two events are said to be independent if the outcome of one has no effect on the probability of the outcome of the other, that is, if:

$$P(A|B) = P(A) \quad \text{or} \quad P(B|A) = P(B).$$

If this is not the case, then the events are dependent. For independent events the multiplicative law becomes:

```
                P(A and B) = P(A)P(B)
```

which is another way of checking for independence.

16. A specific implementation of the general formula for conditional proba-
    bility is <u>Bayes' Theorem</u>, which will be of great value in Decision Analy-
    sis (Chapter 12).

17. If the outcome of the probability experiment is described numerically, it
    is called a <u>random variable</u>. A random variable is a function whose
    numerical value depends on the outcome of the experiment. For example,
    if the result of flipping three coins is recorded as a sequence of heads
    and tails, it is referred to as an event. If we count the heads, the
    number of heads is a random variable. The random variable may assign a
    unique number to each simple event in the sample space or it may assign
    several sample points the same number (e.g., the head-tail sequences HHT,
    HTH, and THH would all be assigned the value 2 if we are counting heads).
    The probability that the random variable has a specific numerical value
    is simply the sum of the probabilities of the sample points that are
    matched with that number. (P(Number of heads = 2) = P(HHT) + P(HTH) +
    P(THH) = 1/8 + 1/8 + 1/8 = 3/8.) The function that gives the probabili-
    ties associated with the possible values for the random variable is
    called a <u>probability distribution</u>.

18. A random variable may be discrete or continuous. A <u>discrete</u> random vari-
    able can only take on certain specific values, between which there are
    gaps. A common example is a variable which must be a nonnegative inte-
    ger. A continuous random variable may take on any real value within a
    specific range. An example is a variable which measures how long it
    takes to perform some activity; time is continuous.

19. A <u>cumulative probability distribution</u> gives the probability that a random
    variable takes on a value less than or equal to a specific number. For
    discrete random variables this is found by adding the individual proba-
    bilities of the values of the variable that are less than or equal to the
    one of interest:

$$P(X \leq x) = F(x) = \sum_{x_i \leq x} P(x_i)$$

For a continuous variable it is found by integration.

20. A very useful discrete probability distribution is the <u>binomial</u>. It is
    used to find the probabilities of the possible numbers of "successes" in
    a fixed number of "trials" of some <u>Bernoulli process</u>. In a Bernoulli
    process, the outcome of an experiment is classified as being of one of
    two types, called "success" and "failure." For example, a coin flip
    results in a head (success) or a tail (failure). The probability of a
    success, p, is the same on every trial. The binomial distribution is
    used to find the probability that there will be exactly x successes in n
    trials:

$$P(x) = (_nC_x)(p^x q^{n-x}) \quad \text{for } x=0,1,2, \ldots ,n$$

where: x is the number of successes
       n is the number of trials
       p is the probability of success on each trial
       q = 1-p is the probability of a failure on each trial
       $_nC_x = n!/(x!(n-x)!)$, 0!=1

21. The Poisson distribution is used when we can count the number of times something does happen but cannot count the number of times it doesn't (e.g., we can count the number of customers who enter a bank office during an hour, but we cannot count the number who don't). The Poisson distribution is useful in queuing theory (Chapter 14). The conditions under which the Poisson distribution applies are:
a. During any interval of length, t, the probability of an occurrence of the event of interest is a constant.
b. The occurrence of an event in any interval is independent of its occurrence in any other interval.
c. The probability of occurrence in an interval of given small size is approximately proportional to the size of that interval.
The probability distribution function is:

$$P(x) = e^{-m}m^x/x! \quad \text{for } x=0,1,2,\ldots$$

where: x is the number of occurrences of the event in a given interval
m is the mean number of occurrences in an interval of that size
e is the base of the natural logarithms

22. With continuous random variables, probability is only defined for ranges. It doesn't make any sense to talk about the probability that the variable equals a specific value, only the probability that it is between specific, distinct values. Thus probability is defined in terms of the cumulative distribution, the rate of change of which is given by a probability density function. Probabilities for ranges are found by finding the area under a probability density function curve between the limits of interest for the variable.

23. One continuous random variable of interest in OR/MS is the uniform or rectangular distribution, for which the probability is evenly distributed over a fixed, limited range. The density function is:

$$f(x) = \begin{cases} \dfrac{1}{b-a} & \text{for } a \leq x \leq b \\\\ 0 & \text{elsewhere} \end{cases}$$

and the cumulative probability function is:

$$F(x) = \begin{cases} 0 & \text{for } x < a \\\\ \dfrac{x-a}{b-a} & \text{for } a \leq x \leq b \\\\ 1 & \text{for } x > b. \end{cases}$$

The uniform distribution is important for simulation (Chapter 15).

24. The normal or Gaussian distribution is probably the most important and useful of all because it:
a. does a good job of describing many natural random phenomena,
b. can be used to approximate other distributions, and
c. forms the basis for much statistical testing and estimation due to the Central Limit Theorem.
The normal distribution has two parameters, its mean μ and its standard deviation σ.

25. Normal distribution probabilities are calculated by using tables since the density function cannot be integrated directly. To use the tables, we make the following transformation

$$Z = \frac{X - \mu}{\sigma}$$

to convert into the <u>standard</u> normal distribution with mean 0 and standard deviation 1. A table for the standard normal distribution is in Appendix C of the text.

KEY TERMS

Match each term with the appropriate definition below.

<u>Terms</u>

_____ 1. additive law

_____ 2. additivity

_____ 3. Bernoulli trial

_____ 4. binomial distribution

_____ 5. collectively exhaustive

_____ 6. complementary event

_____ 7. completeness

_____ 8. compound event

_____ 9. conditional probability

_____ 10. cumulative probability distribution

_____ 11. event

_____ 12. independent events

_____ 13. joint probability

_____ 14. marginal probability

_____ 15. multiplicative law

_____ 16. mutually exclusive

_____ 17. nonnegativity

_____ 18. objective probability

_____ 19. Poisson distribution

_____ 20. probability density function

_____ 21. probability distribution

_____ 22. probability mass function

_____ 23. random variable

_____ 24. sample point

_____ 25. sample space

_____ 26. simple event

_____ 27. standard normal

_____ 28. subjective probability

_____ 29. uniform distribution

<u>Definitions</u>

A. The probability of the entire sample space equals 1.

B. The probability function of a continuous variable.

C. An event consisting of a single outcome.

151

D.   The probability of the simultaneous occurrence of two events.

E.   A function that assigns a numerical value to the outcome of a probability experiment.

F.   Two events with no simple events in common.

G.   A continuous distribution in which all possible values are equally likely.

H.   A discrete distribution used to find the probability of a specific number of successes in a fixed number of trials.

I.   The probability of one outcome or another is the sum of their individual probabilities minus the probability that both occur.

J.   A function that describes the likelihood of alternative values of a discrete random variable.

K.   A function that gives the probability that a random variable will have a value less than or equal to a specific number.

L.   A compound event containing all simple events that are not members of some other specific compound event.

M.   Probability values based on an individual's past experience and intuition.

N.   An event composed of a collection of simple events.

O.   The outcome of a probability experiment.

P.   The set of all possible outcomes of a probability experiment.

Q.   The principle that the probability that either of two mutually exclusive events occurs is the sum of their individual probabilities.

R.   The joint probability of two events is the product of the probability of the first event times the conditional probability of the second event given the first.

S.   The probability of any event is between 0 and 1.

T.   Two events for which the knowledge of one doesn't affect the probability of the other.

U.   A normal probability function with mean 0 and standard deviation 1.

V.   A set of events that, among them, contain all sample points.

W.   Probability based on historical information or rigorous analysis.

X.   A function that describes the relative likelihood of the possible values of a random variable.

Y.   A single outcome of a probability experiment.

Z.   An experiment resulting in one of two possible mutually exclusive out-
     comes.

AA. A probability mass function used for a variable that counts the number of
     occurrences of some event over time or in space.

BB. The probability of one event given the knowledge that a second event has
     occurred.

CC. The probability of a single event occurring.

SOLVED PROBLEM

A manufacturer of stereo equipment has recently been experiencing some problems with the quality of their product. They have been receiving a number of
complaints of mechanical and electrical problems from their customers.
Therefore, they tested a sample of 250 tape recorders and 250 turntables from
their current production; from this sample, they derived the following information:

	Tape Recorders	Turntables
No defects	205	190
Mechanical defect only	25	15
Electrical defect only	10	18
Both mechanical and electrical defects	10	9
	250	250

a.   Based on this sample, what is the probability that a unit (tape recorder
     or turntable) will have a mechanical defect only?

b.   What is the probability that a unit will have both mechanical and elec-
     trical defects given it is a tape recorder?

c.   What is the probability that a particular unit has no defects and is a
     tape recorder?

d.   What is the probability that a unit will not have a defect?

Solution

First, let us define six different events:
     A = unit has no defects
     B = unit has mechanical defects only
     C = unit has electrical defects only
     D = unit has both mechanical and electrical defects

     X = unit is a tape recorder
     Y = unit is a turntable

To analyze this problem, it may be easier to illustrate the data in the form
of probabilities:

	X	Y	
A	.41	.38	.79
B	.05	.03	.08
C	.02	.06	.08
D	.02	.03	.05
	.50	.50	

The column and row totals are now marginal probabilities.

a. The required probability, P(B), is an unconditional or marginal probability and can be found in the margin of row B in the table above.
   P(mechanical defect only) = 0.08

b. This is a conditional probability, P(D|X) = P(D and X)/P(X). The first probability on the right-hand side of the equation, P(D and X) is a joint probability and can be found in the table at row D and column X (0.02). The second, P(X), is another marginal probability and is found as the total of the X column (0.50). Therefore,
   P(D|X) = P(D and X)/P(X) = 0.02/0.50 = 0.04

c. This is a joint probability and can be read directly from the table at row A and column X.
   P(A and X) = 0.41

d. This probability is the complement of the probability of no defects, P(A). P(A) is a marginal probability (0.79) and can be found in the margin of the table. Therefore:

   P($\overline{A}$) = 1 - P(A) = 1 - 0.79 = 0.21

REVIEW EXERCISES

1. In a certain community of 1,000 families, 300 subscribe to Time, 200 subscribe to Sports Illustrated, and 100 subscribe to both magazines. If a family in this community is selected at random, what is the probability that it:
   a. subscribes to either magazine?
   b. subscribes to neither magazine?
   c. subscribes to Sports Illustrated given that it subscribes to Time?
   d. Are the magazine subscriptions independent?

2. In a batch of 10 tax statements being sent out by the county tax office there are two with errors in them. If three are selected at random without replacement, what is the probability that:
   a. there will be none with an error?
   b. three will be exactly one with an error?

3. Suppose that the county sends out several thousand tax statements, of which 20 percent are in error. Reanswer the questions in Exercise 2.

4. A machine breaks down due to the failure of a certain part on an average of once every two days. What is the probability that the machine will not fail at all on a given day?

*5. For the machine in Exercise 4, how many spare parts should be available at the start of a day if the company wants to be 95 percent sure that they have sufficient parts available to handle any failures due to that part on that day?

6. The salespeople for a company average $600,000 in sales per year with a standard deviation of $50,000, sales per person being normally distributed.
a. What is the probability that an individual salesperson will sell between $550,000 and $700,000 in a year?
b. If the company wants to give an award to the top ten percent of salespeople based on the amount of sales, at what level must a salesperson sell in order to qualify for the award?

CHAPTER TEST

1. A random variable is called discrete because:
a. it has only finitely many possible values.
b. there are gaps between possible values.
c. there are values that cannot occur.
d. all of the above.

2. In the past one out of every ten units produced by a particular machine has been defective. The operator states that there is a probability of .10 that the next unit will be defective. This probability is:
a. objective.
b. subjective.
c. joint.
d. conditional.

3. A and B are events defined on a sample space S. If P(A) = .60, P(B) = .50, and P(A and B) = 0, then:
a. P(A or B) = 1.10.
b. P(A or B) = .10.
c. P(A or B) = .30.
d. Something is wrong.

4. There are 10 toasters in plain boxes. Four are white and six are gold. Two boxes are selected and opened. The probability that both boxes contain gold toasters is:
a. .60
b. .333
c. .867
d. .5333

5. A and B are events defined on a sample space S. If P(A) = .5, P(B) = .4, and P(A and B) = .25, then:
a. A and B are mutually exclusive.
b. A and B are collectively exhaustive.
c. A and B are independent.
d. None of the above.

6. In a binomial distribution with eight trials and probability of success of .35, the probability that there will be exactly one success is:
   a. .35
   b. 1.0
   c. .1691
   d. .1372

7. The number of calls arriving at a telephone switchboard during one minute follows a Poisson distribution with m = 1.5. The probability that there will be four calls in the next two minutes is:
   a. .815
   b. .168
   c. .981
   d. .047

8. In a normal distribution with μ = 100 and σ = 12, the probability that 70 $\leq$ x $\leq$ 115 is:
   a. .8882
   b. .8944
   c. .0994
   d. .1118

9. For the normal distribution in Question 8, the value above which there is a 90 percent chance that x will fall is:
   a. 98.72
   b. 90
   c. 84.64
   d. 115.36

10. The average number of accidents at a particular intersection is .10 per day. The appropriate probability distribution to use for finding the probability that there will be two accidents at that intersection during one week (seven days) is:
    a. normal.
    b. Poisson.
    c. uniform.
    d. binomial.

ANSWER KEY

Terms

1. I	7. A	13. D	19. AA	25. P
2. Q	8. N	14. CC	20. B	26. C or Y
3. Z	9. BB	15. R	21. X	27. U
4. H	10. K	16. F	22. J	28. M
5. V	11. O	17. S	23. E	29. G
6. L	12. T	18. W	24. Y or C	

Review Exercises

1. Given P(T) = .3, P(S) = .2, P(T and S) = .1

   a. P(T or S) = P(T) + P(S) - P(T and S)
                = .3 + .2 - .1 = .4

b. $P(\overline{T \text{ or } S}) = 1 - P(T \text{ or } S) = 1 - .4 = .6$

c. $P(S|T) = \dfrac{P(S \text{ and } T)}{P(T)} = \dfrac{.1}{.3} = .333$

d. Not independent since $P(S|T) = .333 \neq .2 = P(S)$

2. a. P(no error at all) = (8/10)(7/9)(6/8) = .4667

    b. P(exactly one error) = P(error on first only)
$$\begin{aligned}
&\qquad\qquad\qquad\qquad + P(\text{error on second only}) \\
&\qquad\qquad\qquad\qquad + P(\text{error on third only}) \\
&= (2/10)(8/9)(7/8) + (8/10)(2/9)(7/8) \\
&\qquad\qquad + (8/10)(7/9)(2/8) \\
&= .4667
\end{aligned}$$

3. Use a binomial distribution with n=3, p=.20.
    a. P(X=0) = .5120   from Appendix D of text
    b. P(X=1) = .3840   from Appendix D of text

4. Use a Poisson distribution with m = .50/day
    P(X=0) = .607   from Appendix E of text

5. Determine the value of c such that $P(X \leq c) \geq .95$, given m = .5.

c	$P(X \leq c)$
0	.607
1	.910
2	.986 > .95

They should have two spares available.

6. X is a normal variable with μ = 600,000 and σ = 50,000.

    a. $P(550,000 \leq X \leq 700,000)$

$$= P\left(\frac{550,000-600,000}{50,000} \leq Z \leq \frac{700,000-600,000}{50,000}\right)$$

$$= P(-1.00 \leq Z \leq 2.00)$$
$$= .9772 - .1587 = .8185 \qquad \text{from Appendix C}$$

b. First we find the value of Z above which the probability is .10 and then use $Z = (X-\mu)/\sigma$ to solve for X.

From Appendix C, the 90th percentile (10 percent above) value for Z is 1.28.

$$1.28 = \frac{X-600,000}{50,000} \qquad \text{so} \qquad X = \$664,000$$

Chapter Test

1. b	3. d	5. d	7. b	9. c
2. a	4. b	6. d	8. a	10. b

CHAPTER TWELVE

DECISION THEORY

MAIN POINTS

1. Most complex management decisions involve choosing from among several previously identified different courses of action in an environment of uncertainty. Decision theory is a methodology for dealing with this situation.

2. Application areas include natural resource development, finance, marketing, production, agriculture, and personal decisions--a wide variety.

3. Decision theory problems generally involve discrete decision alternatives and probabilistic events (states of nature) that affect the desirability of the outcomes of the decisions that can be made.

4. The analysis begins with the three steps of identifying the decision alternatives, defining the states of nature that can affect the quality of the outcome, and computing the value or payoff (gain or loss) of each decision-state of nature combination. The outcomes are often expressed in a payoff table or matrix.

5. Much of the value of decision theory is that it requires a systematic and rational structuring of the information relevant to a decision.

6. In some cases, the decision maker cannot estimate probabilities for the states of nature. For this case, a variety of decision making procedures have been developed. Among them are the maximin, maximax, and minimax regret criteria.

7. The maximin gain (or minimax loss) criterion is very conservative. It selects the decision alternative which has the largest worst gain (smallest worst loss).

8. The maximax gain (or minimin loss) criterion is optimistic. It selects the decision alternative which has the largest best gain (or smallest least loss).

9. The minimax regret criterion begins with finding the regret for each decision-state of nature combination. This is defined to be the difference between the value of that combination and the value that would have been obtained if the best decision had been made for that state of nature. The minimax rule is applied to the regret table to choose the alternative.

10. In most cases, the decision maker can assign probabilities to the states of nature. In this case, the relevant decision criterion is the maximization of expected gain or the minimization of expected loss, depending on the value formulation used.

11. If the payoff is measured in money, the decision chosen is the one with the maximum (if gain) or minimum (if cost) expected monetary value (EMV):

$$EMV = \sum_{i=1}^{k} p(s_i)x_i$$

where $p(s_i)$ is the probability of state of nature i and x_i is the monetary value of implementing the decision being evaluated in state of nature i.

12. Rather than using a payoff matrix, the decision problem can be presented in a decision tree. Its advantages relative to a payoff matrix are greater flexibility in showing probability distributions for the states of nature, which may vary depending on the decision being considered, and the ability to represent multistage decision problems more easily.

13. The four basic components of a decision tree are decision nodes (shown as squares), chance nodes (shown as circles), alternative branches to show the possibilities at a decision point, and probabilistic branches to show the possible states of nature and their probabilities.

14. Analysis with a decision tree involves evaluating all decision and chance nodes. The value of a chance node is the expected value of the probabilistic branches coming from it. The value of a decision node is the value of the best alternative branch starting from it.

15. The evaluation of a decision tree starts at its extreme right side, working back toward the start of the tree, replacing each branching from a node by the value of that node as described. This process is known as "averaging out and folding back." By working back to the start of the tree in this way, the decision maker traces a path of decisions in reverse order, leading eventually to the best initial decision.

16. Most real world decision problems include the option of obtaining additional information at a cost. This added information can change the probabilities of the states of nature, thus possibly changing the EMVs of the alternatives.

17. When additional information is available there are two decisions to make: first, whether or not to buy the information, and second, how to use it in making decisions. Answering the first question depends on first getting answers to the second.

18. One way of making this pair of decisions is with a decision tree, including the decision about buying the information in the early stages of the tree and the choices among decision alternatives in the latter part of the tree.

19. The use of the available information in decision making requires the reassessment of state-of-nature probabilities as the result of the different types of information that might be received. This is done by using Bayes' Theorem:

$$P(A_i|B) = \frac{P(B|A_i)P(A_i)}{\sum_{j=1}^{k} P(B|A_j)P(A_j)}$$

160

where A_i is a particular state of nature (of which there are k) and B is a known event. The probabilities developed using Bayes' Theorem are called posterior or a posteriori probabilities because they are probabilities after the information is received. The probabilities without the new information are called prior or a priori probabilities.

20. In evaluating the use of the additional information, its cost is subtracted from the applicable payoffs at the end of the tree.

21. The expected value of sample or imperfect information (EVSI) is the difference between the expected values of the best decision strategies with and without the information. To find the total (as opposed to net) EVSI, the cost of the information would be added back into the expected value of the decision using the information.

22. The expected value of perfect information (EVPI) is useful as an upper bound on the value of sample information.

23. When significant amounts of money are involved, many decision makers will not act to maximize EMV. They are risk takers or risk averters. A risk taker or gambler will choose an alternative that may have a negative EMV in order to have a chance at a high payoff. A risk averter will pay to avoid a chance situation with a zero or small positive EMV.

24. To evaluate a decision problem for a non-EMVer, the monetary outcomes in the tree are replaced by their utilities. These utilities are developed by finding certainty equivalents.

25. A certainty equivalent is the certain or sure amount that one would accept instead of a probabilistic combination of the best and worst payoffs possible in the problem. For a risk averter, the certainty equivalent is less than the EMV of the best-worst combination. For a risk taker it is more.

26. A way of handling decision problems with continuous states of nature is to simulate the decision tree with a computer, using a randomly selected value at each chance node and repeating the process many times.

27. Since the quality of the decision may be highly dependent on the quality of the probability assessments for the chance nodes, the decision maker should be aware of the level of sensitivity of the decision made to minor changes in the probabilities used.

SUGGESTED READINGS

An excellent introduction to the concepts and use of Decision Theory, including a description of the development of utility values, can be found in:

Raiffa, Howard, Decision Analysis: Introductory Lectures on Choices Under Uncertainty, (Reading, MA: Addison-Wesley Publishing, 1968).

A recent review on the development of and the scope of decision theory (with extensive references) can be found in:

Fishburn, Peter C., "Foundations of Decision Analysis: Along the Way," Management Science, v. 35, n. 4 (April 1989), pp. 387-405.

The January-February 1980 issue of Operations Research (v. 28, n. 1) is devoted to the topic of Decision Analysis. It includes application articles as well as conceptual articles. Additional application articles are:

Alemi, F., and J. Agliato, "Restricting Patients' Choices of Physicians: A Decision Analytic Evaluation of Costs," Interfaces, v. 19, n. 2 (March-April 1989), pp. 20-28.

Bell, D. E., "Bidding for the S. S. Kuniang," Interfaces, v. 14, n. 2 (April 1984), pp. 17-28.

Cohan, D., S. M. Haas, D. L. Radloff, and R. F. Yancik, "Using Fire in Forest Management: Decision Making Under Uncertainty," Interfaces, v. 14, n. 5 (September-October 1984), pp. 8-19.

deRivera, D. P. S., "Decision Analysis Model for a Serious Medical Problem," Management Science, v. 26, n. 7 (July 1980), pp. 707-718.

Ulvila, J. W., "Postal Automation (ZIP + 4) Technology: A Decision Analysis," Interfaces, v. 17, n. 2 (March-April 1987), pp. 1-12.

KEY TERMS

Match each term with the correct definition below.

Terms

_____ 1. a posteriori probability

_____ 2. Bayes' Theorem

_____ 3. certainty equivalent

_____ 4. chance node

_____ 5. decision alternatives

_____ 6. decision node

_____ 7. decision tree

_____ 8. expected monetary value

_____ 9. expected value of sample information

_____ 10. maximax criterion

_____ 11. maximin criterion

_____ 12. minimax regret criterion

_____ 13. payoff matrix

_____ 14. risk averter

_____ 15. risk taker

_____ 16. states of nature

Definitions

A. Choosing the decision alternative with the largest "smallest payoff."

B. A decision maker who requires a certainty equivalent exceeding the EMV to give up a chance outcome.

C. A tree diagram representation of a decision theory problem.

D. The aspects of a decision situation over which the decision maker has no control.

E. The probabilistic combination of the monetary payoffs from a decision alternative.

F. A procedure for reassessing probabilities to reflect additional information obtained.

G. The choices from which the decision maker must select an action.

H. A tabular representation of the payoffs resulting from the decision alternative-state of nature combinations.

I. A branching point in a decision tree from which start probabilistic branches.

J. A branching point in a decision tree from which start decision alternative branches.

K. Choosing the decision alternative with the largest "largest payoff."

L. The amount of money one requires to forego a probabilistic combination of good and bad payoffs.

M. The increase in EMV from using imperfect information to revise probabilities in a decision problem.

N. A probability resulting from the application of Bayes' Theorem.

O. A decision maker who will accept a certainty equivalent lower than the EMV of a chance outcome.

P. Choosing the decision alternative which gives the smallest "largest difference from the best payoff for a state of nature."

SOLVED PROBLEM

A local retailer of appliances purchases toasters in lots of fifty units. The supplier of these toasters occasionally provides "bad" lots due to a problem with the manufacturing process; in this situation, the defective rate of the process is twenty percent. On the other hand, when the production process is operating properly and producing "good" lots, only five percent of the units are defective. The manufacturer provides "bad" lots six percent of the time. The retailer has now decided that three toasters should be sampled from each lot and tested. If any of these units are found to be defective, the entire lot will be rejected and sent back to the manufacturer.

a. What is the probability that the lot will be accepted (all sampled units are not defective) given that the sample was from a "good" lot?

b. Given that the sampled units are not defective, what is the probability that the lot is a "good" lot? from a "bad" lot?

c. What is the probability that the lot will be accepted?

Solution

a. Since the units sampled are either defective or not defective, the testing can be considered a Bernoulli trial (see Chapter 11). The probability of a success (no defectives) from a good lot is 95 percent; the probability of a failure (at least one defective) is 5 percent. The lot will be accepted if none of the sampled units are defective, so:

$$P(x) = (_nC_x)(p^x q^{n-x})$$

$$P(x=0|good) = (_3C_3)(p^3 q^{3-3}) = [3!/(3!0!)](.95)^3(.05)^{3-3} = 0.857$$

b. This is an "a posteriori" probability. We use Bayes' theorem to revise the prior probabilities.

$$P(Good|x=0) = \frac{P(x=0|Good)P(Good)}{P(x=0|Good)P(Good) + P(x=0|Bad)P(Bad)}$$

$$= \frac{(0.857)(0.94)}{(0.857)(0.94) + (0.512)(0.06)} = 0.963$$

$$P(Bad|x=0) = \frac{P(x=0|Bad)P(Bad)}{P(x=0|Good)P(Good) + P(x=0|Bad)P(Bad)}$$

$$= \frac{(0.512)(0.06)}{(0.857)(0.94) + (0.512)(0.06)} = 0.037$$

So based on this sample, if none of the units sampled are defective, the a posteriori probability of the lot being "good" increased from 94 percent to over 96 percent.

c. We can find the marginal probability of lot acceptance (no defectives) as:

$$P(x=0) = P(x=0|Good)P(Good) + P(x=0|Bad)P(Bad)$$
$$= (0.857)(0.94) + (0.512)(0.06)$$
$$= 0.837$$

REVIEW EXERCISES

1. Given the following payoff matrices, find the recommended decision for each of the following criteria (assume the payoffs are gains):
   a. Maximin
   b. Maximax
   c. Minimax regret

Payoff Matrix

Decision Alternatives	States of Nature			
	s_1	s_2	s_3	s_4
d_1	100	150	200	400
d_2	300	100	200	250
d_3	200	200	250	200

2. Assume that the payoff matrix in Question 1 represents <u>losses</u> rather than gains. Find the recommended decision under each of the following criteria:
   a. Minimax
   b. Minimin
   c. Minimax regret

3. Assume that the following probabilities apply to the states of nature in Question 1:

State of Nature	Probability
s_1	.2
s_2	.3
s_3	.4
s_4	.1

   Determine the best decision under the EMV criterion.

4. Farmer Brown is planning his land use for the coming year. Of interest is his north field. The value of particular uses will depend most heavily on the amount of rainfall during the growing season. Farmer Brown classifies the rainfall as either light, normal, or heavy.

   Available to Farmer Brown are three possible uses for the field. He could plant corn or soybeans or leave it in pasture for cows. The payoff matrix below represents Farmer Brown's best assessment of the gains from each use-rainfall combination.

   Payoff Matrix

		Rainfall	
Use	Light	Normal	Heavy
Corn	100	500	300
Soybeans	300	300	200
Pasture	150	300	400

   Based on Farmer Brown's recollection of the past several years, he assigns the following probabilities to the rainfall possibilities:

Rainfall	Probability
Light	.3
Normal	.6
Heavy	.1

   Using these probabilities, what should Farmer Brown do?

5. Construct a decision tree for Farmer Brown.

6. A weather forecasting service has sent Farmer Brown some promotional material. It claims to be able to forecast the long term (growing season) weather with high, although not perfect, accuracy. According to their literature, they have the following prediction probabilities relative to the true weather conditions:

165

| | True Weather Conditions | | |
Forecast	Light	Normal	Heavy
Light	.7	.1	.1
Normal	.2	.8	.3
Heavy	.1	.1	.6
	1.0	1.0	1.0

Assuming that these quoted accuracy probabilities are correct, find the revised (a posteriori) probabilities of the weather conditions given a forecast of:

a. Light

b. Normal

c. Heavy

7. The forecasting service charges 10 for its prediction. Should Farmer Brown pay for the forecast?

*8. The Ajax Manufacturing Company is purchasing a new custom-built production machine. One of the components in this machine is a special gear assembly which, due to the specialized nature of the machine, is not available as a stock item from any distributor. If replacement gear assemblies are ever needed, they will have to be custom made at the time of need.

Ajax's engineers are trying to decide whether to buy extra gear assemblies at the time of purchase of the machine and, if so, how many. A gear assembly bought at the time of purchase of the machine will cost $5000. If one is required in the future, the cost will be higher. In addition, there will be an equipment shutdown and lost production. Considering these two types of costs and the fact that they will be in the future, the engineers, in consultation with the finance department, have estimated a present value of $50,000 for a breakdown with no available spare gear assembly.

After consultation with the engineers from the machine supplier, the engineers have determined that it is reasonable to use a Poisson distribution with mean failure rate equal to .5 for the number of gear assembly failures over the life of the equipment.

How many spare gear assemblies should be ordered with the machine, if any? Assume that, if gear assemblies are bought in the future, they will be bought as required.

9. By working hard for many years and saving their money, the Scott family has managed to accumulate $100,000. Their dream has always been to own their own restaurant. This is enough money for them to do so. They must now decide whether to put the money into starting a restaurant. They have done extensive financial analyses and have developed the payoff matrix below.

Payoff Matrix

| | Acceptance Level | | |
Decision	Low	Medium	High
Open	5	200	500
Not Open	100	100	100

The payoffs are expressed in thousands of dollars.

The Scott's have been following the local restaurant market for several years. Based on this they have assessed the probabilities of acceptance of their restaurant to be:

Acceptance	Probability
Low	.5
Medium	.4
High	.1

a. Develop a decision tree for the Scott's problem.
b. Based on EMV, should they open a restaurant or not?

10. In order to better assess the acceptance probabilities, the Scott's have contacted a local market research firm. The market research firm will prepare a report indicating that the community reaction to the proposed restaurant will be Positive or Negative. Based on their discussions with other clients of this firm, the Scott's develop accuracy assessments of the firm's reports as follows:

Report	True Acceptance level		
	Low	Medium	High
Positive	.2	.6	.9
Negative	.8	.4	.1

Develop a posteriori probability distributions under the assumption that the report is:

a. Positive
b. Negative

11. If the market research firm will charge $5000 (a payoff of -5) for performing the study, what should the Scott's do about having the study performed and opening the restaurant?

*12. The Scott's are rather concerned about the prospect of losing the money they have worked and saved for so long. After considerable deliberation, they have concluded that a more reasonable representation of the true worth of the money to them is not its actual value but the square root of the number of thousands (e.g., $100,000 has as its true value the square root of 100, which is 10). Using this utility function (an alternative to the certainty equivalent p values discussed in the text), resolve Questions 9 and 11. Should the Scott's open their restaurant?

CHAPTER TEST

1. Decision theory analysis:
   a. can only be applied when probabilities are known.
   b. is applicable only to business problems.
   c. is a way of coping with an uncertain environment.
   d. develops decision alternatives for the decision maker.

The following payoff matrix is to be used in Questions 2 through 5.

167

Payoff Matrix

Decision Alternatives	States of Nature		
	s_1	s_2	s_3
d_1	100	50	20
d_2	10	40	60
d_3	40	50	30
d_4	20	70	20

2. If the maximin criterion is used, the appropriate decision is:
   a. d_1
   b. d_2
   c. d_3
   d. d_4

3. If the maximax criterion is used, the appropriate decision is:
   a. d_1
   b. d_2
   c. d_3
   d. d_4

4. If the minimax regret criterion is used, the appropriate decision is:
   a. d_1
   b. d_2
   c. d_3
   d. d_4

5. Assume that $P(s_1) = .1$, $P(s_2) = .3$, and $P(s_3) = .6$. The decision that maximizes expected value is:
   a. d_1
   b. d_2
   c. d_3
   d. d_4

6. All decision trees include:
   a. decision nodes.
   b. chance nodes.
   c. probabilities.
   d. all of the above.

7. Most real world decision problems:
   a. involve uncertainty.
   b. include the possibility of obtaining additional information.
   c. may have the state-of-nature probabilities changed by added information.
   d. all of the above.

8. The probabilities resulting from using Bayes' Theorem are:
   a. prior probabilities.
   b. joint probabilities.
   c. a posteriori probabilities.
   d. marginal probabilities.

9. The difference between EMV with imperfect information and EMV with no information is called the:
   a. expected value of perfect information.
   b. expected value of sample information.
   c. certainty equivalent.
   d. a posteriori distribution.

10. A risk averter:
   a. assigns a certainty equivalent below the EMV of a gamble.
   b. assigns a certainty equivalent above the EMV of a gamble.
   c. assigns a certainty equivalent equal to the EMV of a gamble.
   d. prefers any sure thing to a gamble.

ANSWER KEY

Terms

1. N	4. I	7. C	10. K	13. H	16. D
2. F	5. G	8. E	11. A	14. O	
3. L	6. J	9. M	12. P	15. B	

Review Exercises

1.

a.

Alternative	Minimum Payoff
d_1	100
d_2	100
d_3	200*

Recommended decision: d_3

b.

Alternative	Maximum Payoff
d_1	400*
d_2	300
d_3	250

Recommended decision: d_1

c. Regret Matrix

Alternative	s_1	s_2	s_3	s_4	Maximum
d_1	200	50	50	0	200
d_2	0	100	50	150	150*
d_3	100	0	0	200	200

Recommended decision: d_2

169

2.

a.

Alternative	Maximum
d_1	400
d_2	300
d_3	250*

Recommended decision: d_3

b.

Alternative	Minimum
d_1	100*
d_2	100*
d_3	200

Recommended decision: d_1 and d_2 tie

c.

Regret Matrix

Alternative	s_1	s_2	s_3	s_4	Maximum
d_1	0	50	0	200	200
d_2	200	0	0	50	200
d_3	100	100	50	0	100*

Recommended decision: d_3

3. $EMV(d_1) = .2(100) + .3(150) + .4(200) + .1(400) = 185$

$EMV(d_2) = .2(300) + .3(100) + .4(200) + .1(250) = 195$

$EMV(d_3) = .2(200) + .3(200) + .4(250) + .1(200) = 220*$

Recommended decision: d_3

4. $EMV(\text{corn}) = .3(100) + .6(500) + .1(300) = 360*$
$EMV(\text{soybeans}) = .3(300) + .6(300) + .1(200) = 290$
$EMV(\text{pasture}) = .3(150) + .6(300) + .1(400) = 265$

Farmer Brown should plant corn.

5.

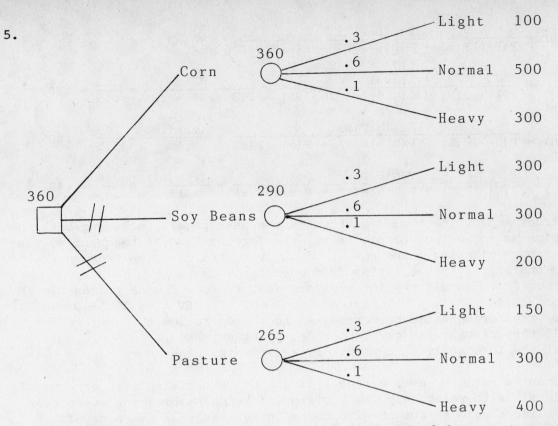

6. To simplify the notation used, we will use capital letters to represent the <u>true</u> weather conditions - L for light, N for normal, and H for heavy rain - and lower case letters for the weather service's forecast - l for light forecast, n for normal forecast, and h for heavy forecast. Use Bayes' Theorem to find the a posteriori probabilities.

a.
$$P(L|l) = \frac{P(l|L)P(L)}{P(l|L)P(L) + P(l|N)P(N) + P(l|H)P(H)}$$

$$= \frac{(.7)(.3)}{(.7)(.3) + (.1)(.6) + (.1)(.1)} = \frac{.21}{.21 + .06 + .01} = \frac{.21}{.28} = .75$$

$$P(N|l) = \frac{P(l|N)P(N)}{P(l|L)P(L) + P(l|N)P(N) + P(l|H)P(H)} = \frac{(.1)(.6)}{.28} = \frac{.06}{.28} = .214$$

$$P(H|l) = \frac{P(l|H)P(H)}{P(l|L)P(L) + P(l|N)P(N) + P(l|H)P(H)} = \frac{(.1)(.1)}{.28} = \frac{.01}{.28} = .036$$

b.
$$P(L|n) = \frac{P(n|L)P(L)}{P(n|L)P(L) + P(n|N)P(N) + P(n|H)P(H)}$$

$$= \frac{(.2)(.3)}{(.2)(.3) + (.8)(.6) + (.3)(.1)} = \frac{.06}{.06 + .48 + .03} = \frac{.06}{.57} = .105$$

$$P(N|n) = \frac{P(n|N)P(N)}{P(n|L)P(L) + P(n|N)P(N) + P(n|H)P(H)} = \frac{(.8)(.6)}{.57} = \frac{.48}{.57} = .842$$

$$P(H|n) = \frac{P(n|H)P(H)}{P(n|L)P(L) + P(n|N)P(N) + P(n|H)P(H)} = \frac{(.3)(.1)}{.57} = \frac{.03}{.57} = .53$$

c.

$$P(L|h) = \frac{P(h|L)P(L)}{P(h|L)P(L) + P(h|N)P(N) + P(h|H)P(H)}$$

$$= \frac{(.1)(.3)}{(.1)(.3) + (.1)(.6) + (.6)(.1)} = \frac{.03}{.03 + .06 + .06} = \frac{.03}{.15} = .20$$

$$P(N|h) = \frac{P(h|N)P(N)}{P(h|L)P(L) + P(h|N)P(N) + P(h|H)P(H)} = \frac{(.1)(.6)}{.15} = \frac{.06}{.15} = .40$$

$$P(H|h) = \frac{P(h|H)P(H)}{P(h|L)P(L) + P(h|N)P(N) + P(h|H)P(H)} = \frac{(.6)(.1)}{.15} = \frac{.06}{.15} = .40$$

7. Construct a decision tree (as shown on the next page), including both the decision as to whether or not to buy the forecast and, subsequently, what to do about planting. The result of applying the decision tree, using the a posteriori probabilities from question 6 is:

    Farmer Brown should pay for the forecast. By so doing he raises his EMV from 360 to 379.1, a net increase of 19.1. The EVSI is 19.1+10 = 29.1. Once the forecast has been received he should follow this strategy:
    If the forecast is for light rain, plant soybeans.
    If the forecast is for normal or heavy rain, plant corn.

8. This can be structured as either a single stage decision tree or a payoff matrix since there is only one decision to be made: How many spare gear assemblies should be bought with the machine? We will use a payoff matrix.

    The states of nature are the number of replacement gear assemblies required over the life of the machine. Since that number is potentially infinite (although integer), we will first use the Poisson distribution with m = .5 (see Chapter 11) to find the probabilities of requiring 0, 1, 2, etc., stopping when the probability becomes small.

Number of Replacements	Probability
0	.607
1	.303
2	.076
3	.013
4	.002

    Since the probabilities for five or more replacements are less than .001, we will ignore them. (These probabilities can be calculated directly or be found by using the table in Appendix E in the text.) We will thus use as our states of nature replacement requirements of 0, 1, 2, 3, or 4. These will also be the decision alternatives. Table entries are in present value of thousands of dollars.

    Payoff Matrix

Spare Gear Assemblies	Replacements Required				
	0	1	2	3	4
0	0	50	100	150	200
1	5	5	55	105	155
2	10	10	10	60	110
3	15	15	15	15	65
4	20	20	20	20	20

172

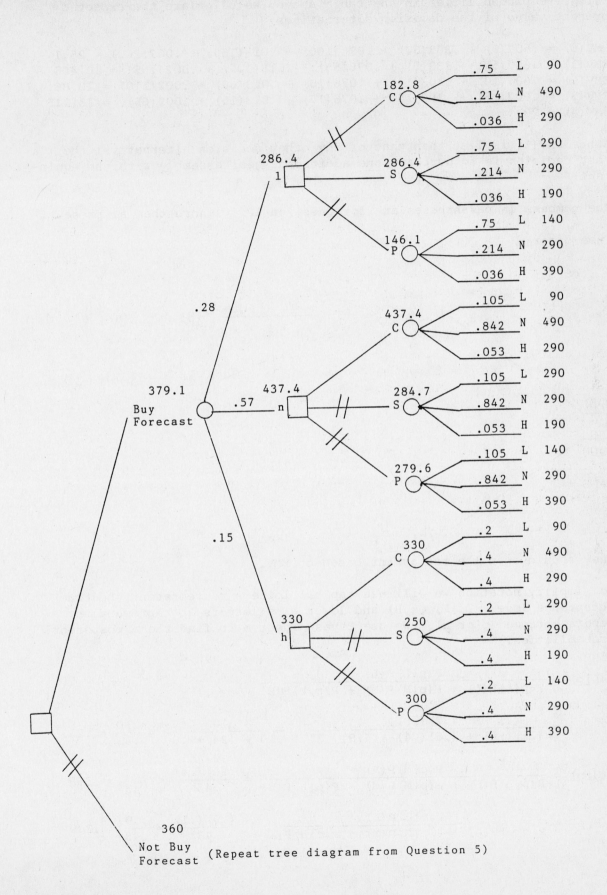

(Repeat tree diagram from Question 5)

173

Using the probabilities in the table above, we calculate the expected present value of the decision alternatives:

EMV(0) = .607(0) + .303(50) + .076(100) + .013(150) + .002(200) = 25.1
EMV(1) = .607(5) + .303(5) + .076(55) + .013(105) + .002(155) = 10.405
EMV(2) = .607(10) + .303(10) + .076(10) + .013(60) + .002(110) = 10.86
EMV(3) = .607(15) + .303(15) + .076(15) + .013(15) + .002(65) = 15.115
EMV(4) = 20

Since EMV(1) is less than that of any other decision alternative, the best decision is to purchase <u>one</u> additional gear assembly with the equipment.

9. The numbers in parentheses are for Question 12. Ignore them at present.

a. Tree diagram

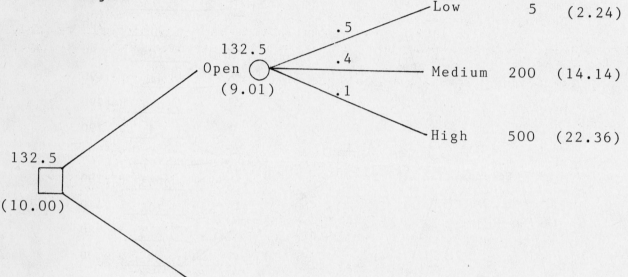

b. They should open the restaurant based on EMV.

10. To simplify notation we will use capital letters to represent the true acceptance level (L, M, or H) and lower case letters to represent the report outcome (p or n). We use Bayes' Theorem to find the a posteriori probabilities.

a.
$$P(L|p) = \frac{P(p|L)P(L)}{P(p|L)P(L) + P(p|M)P(M) + P(p|H)P(H)}$$

$$= \frac{(.2)(.5)}{(.2)(.5) + (.6)(.4) + (.9)(.1)} = \frac{.10}{.10 + .24 + .09} = \frac{.10}{.43} = .233$$

$$P(M|p) = \frac{P(p|M)P(M)}{P(p|L)P(L) + P(p|M)P(M) + P(p|H)P(H)} = \frac{(.6)(.4)}{.43} = \frac{.24}{.43} = .558$$

$$P(H|p) = \frac{P(p|H)P(H)}{P(p|L)P(L) + P(p|M)P(M) + P(p|H)P(H)} = \frac{(.9)(.1)}{.43} = \frac{.09}{.43} = .209$$

b.
$$P(L|n) = \frac{P(n|L)P(L)}{P(n|L)P(L) + P(n|M)P(M) + P(n|H)P(H)}$$

$$= \frac{(.8)(.5)}{(.8)(.5) + (.4)(.4) + (.1)(.1)} = \frac{.40}{.40 + .16 + .01} = \frac{.40}{.57} = .702$$

$$P(M|n) = \frac{P(n|M)P(M)}{P(n|L)P(L) + P(n|M)P(M) + P(n|H)P(H)} = \frac{(.4)(.4)}{.57} = \frac{.16}{.57} = .281$$

$$P(H|n) = \frac{P(n|H)P(H)}{P(n|L)P(L) + P(n|M)P(M) + P(n|H)P(H)} = \frac{(.1)(.1)}{.57} = \frac{.01}{.57} = .018$$

11. Develop a decision tree, including as its first decision stage the question of whether or not to have the study done and as its second decision stage the question of whether or not to open the restaurant.

Based on the analysis represented by this decision tree, the Scott's should pay for a market research study. If the report is positive, they should open the restaurant. If the report is negative, they should not.

The numbers in parentheses are for Question 12. Ignore them at present.

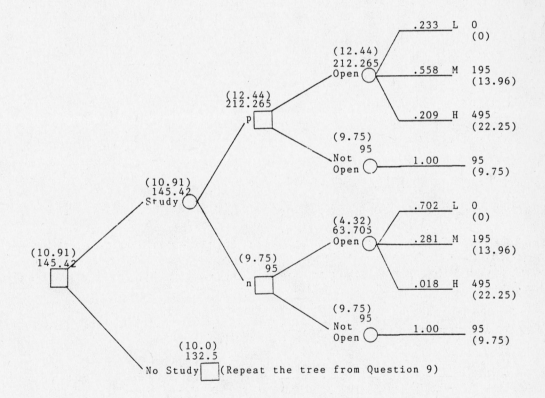

The EMV of following this strategy is $145,420 as opposed to the EMV of $132,500 without the market survey.

12. The decision trees for the utility value versions of Questions 9 and 11 are identical in structure to those shown. The utility values for the final payoffs are found by taking the square root of the monetary payoff values. These utility values, the expected utility values of the chance

175

nodes and the expected utility values of the decision nodes are shown in the tree diagrams for Questions 9 and 11 in parentheses.

For Question 9, without a survey, the decision is reversed. The expected utility of opening a restaurant is lower than the certain utility of not opening the restaurant. Therefore, the restaurant should <u>not</u> be opened.

For Question 11, with the possibility of a survey, the strategy is the same as it was using EMV. The survey should be taken. If the report is positive, the restaurant should be opened. If the report is negative, it should not.

Chapter Test

1. c   3. a   5. b   7. d   9. b
2. c   4. a   6. d   8. c   10. a

CHAPTER THIRTEEN

FORECASTING

MAIN POINTS

1. All productive organizations need accurate and timely forecasts to serve as the basis for planning decisions.

2. One way of categorizing forecasts is by their time horizon. Short-range forecasts (up to one year) are for operational decisions such as production scheduling and short-term financing. Medium-range forecasts (one to three years) are the basis for equipment and personnel decisions. Long-range forecasts (over three years) are needed for decisions with a long lead time such as plant and some equipment.

3. Forecasting techniques are qualitative, time-series analysis, or causal.

4. Qualitative methods, such as the Delphi method, market research, panel consensus, grass-roots forecasting, and historical analogy, are used when quantitative data is unavailable or inappropriate, such as for predicting technological change. They work better for medium- and long-range forecasts than for short-range. The Delphi method and market research tend to be time consuming and expensive.

5. Time-series analysis is based on projecting historical patterns into the future, assuming that the same patterns will continue. Time-series models cannot predict turning points. A time series has four basic components: trend, cyclic, seasonal, and random.

6. Trend is a long term growth or decay pattern. Cyclic is a multi-year, up-and-down pattern tied to the business cycle. Seasonal refers to regular repeated swings around the trend and cycle, repeated in a time frame of a year or less. Random refers to anything that cannot be explained by the other components.

7. Causal models attempt to predict the value of the variable of interest from the values of related, explanatory variables. Multiple regression, econometric, and simulation models are popular types. They are expensive and require a long time to develop, but are more accurate than most other types.

8. In selecting a forecasting model, two types of costs must be recognized: the cost of inaccuracy and the cost of making the forecast. The objective should be to minimize their sum.

9. Besides costs, other factors to consider in selecting a model are the planning horizon, the time to develop the model, and the unavailability of required data.

10. Fairly simple time-series models are popular for short-range forecasting because they are easy and fast to develop, inexpensive, and reasonably accurate in the short term.

11. Moving average models use the average or weighted average of the most recent periods' values to forecast the value for the next period.

12. Exponentially smoothed forecasts tend to be more accurate than moving average models. There are many types of exponentially smoothed models, the most basic of which are simple exponential smoothing, appropriate for data with a basically horizontal pattern and no seasonality, and trend-adjusted, appropriate for a data pattern with a linear trend. The reaction to pattern changes and the influence of random swings in the data is governed by the smoothing constant. A smoothing constant close to zero gives a stable model while a constant close to one is highly reactive.

13. One method for projecting trend in a time series is with a simple regression model, using time as the independent variable. One advantage of this type of model is the ability to estimate a prediction of standard deviation and use it to find a confidence interval for the prediction.

14. Since all forecasts are wrong, it is important to monitor and assess forecast errors to be able to identify abnormal errors and models that are not tracking the data appropriately.

15. Two popular measures of forecast accuracy are (1) the mean absolute deviation or MAD, the average of the absolute values of the forecast errors over several time periods, and (2) the mean squared error or MSE, the average of the absolute values of the forecast errors over several time periods.

16. A tracking signal is useful for detecting that a model is giving forecasts that are consistently either above or below the actual values. The tracking signal is the sum of actual forecast errors over several periods divided by the MAD for the same interval. If the absolute value of the tracking signal exceeds a critical value, usually picked to be between 3.0 and 7.0, it indicates that the model is performing poorly. The lower the critical value is, the more quickly the tracking signal will detect problems.

SUGGESTED READINGS

An excellent basic source on the issues in forecasting and some basic models is:

Wheelwright, S. C. and S. Makridakis, Forecasting Methods for Management (New York: John Wiley & Sons, 1973).

An article to help guide in the selection of an appropriate forecasting technique can be found in:

Georgoff, D. M. and R. G. Murdick, "Manager's Guide to Forecasting," Harvard Business Review, v. 64, n. 1 (January/February 1986), pp. 110-120.

Selected applications are:

Guerard, J. B., Jr., and C. R. Beidleman, "Composite Earnings Forecasting Efficiency," _Interfaces_, v. 17, n. 5 (September-October 1987), pp. 103-113.

Helmer, F. T., "Forecasting Nursing Staffing Requirements by Intensity-of-Care Level," _Interfaces_, v. 10, n. 3 (June 1980), pp. 50-56.

Kallina, C., "Development and Implementation of a Simple Short Range Forecasting Model - a Case Study," _Interfaces_, v. 8, n. 3 (June 1978), pp. 32-41.

Oren, S. S., "Evaluating a New Market: a Forecasting System for Nonimpact Computer Printers," _Interfaces_, v. 10, n. 6 (December 1980), pp. 76-87.

Sarin, R. K., "An Approach for Long Term Forecasting with an Application to Solar Electric Energy," _Management Science_, v. 25, n. 6 (June 1979), pp. 543-554.

KEY TERMS

Match each term with the appropriate definition below.

Terms

_____ 1. causal

_____ 2. cyclic

_____ 3. Delphi method

_____ 4. econometric model

_____ 5. exponential smoothing

_____ 6. grass-roots forecasting

_____ 7. independent variable

_____ 8. MAD

_____ 9. moving average

_____ 10. multiple regression

_____ 11. panel consensus

_____ 12. planning horizon

_____ 13. qualitative technique

_____ 14. random

_____ 15. seasonal

_____ 16. time-series model

_____ 17. tracking signal

_____ 18. trend

Definitions

A. The time-series component representing a regular, repeated pattern in a time frame of a year or less.

B. A forecasting model based on averaging the values from a fixed number of past periods.

C. A forecasting model based on simultaneous estimation of a set of equations.

179

D. A qualitative technique involving discussion among a group of experts to reach an agreement.

E. An external variable used to predict the variable of interest.

F. An indicator used to identify that a forecasting model is not keeping up with the trend in a time series.

G. The time frame for which a model is to produce forecasts.

H. A model type that attempts to explain the values of a variable in terms of the values and attributes of other variables.

I. A qualitative forecasting technique involving successive "blind" exchanges of opinion among experts, attempting to achieve consensus.

J. A time-series model in which forecasts are updated each period by adding a fraction of the difference between the actual and forecasted values to the previous forecast.

K. A time-series component reflecting general movement up or down over many periods.

L. A forecasting model that extrapolates historical data patterns into the future.

M. The time-seies component reflecting up and down movement over several years, following the business cycle.

N. A measure of forecast accuracy that averages the absolute values of forecast errors over several periods.

O. The movement in time-series values that is not explainable by other causes.

P. A qualitative technique that combines estimates by those closest to the area being forecasted.

Q. A class of forecasting techniques useful when there is limited historical data.

R. A forecasting method that predicts the value of one variable as a function of several others.

SOLVED PROBLEM

A small country store has collected the following demand figures for one of their more popular soft drinks.

Year	Demand (in 000s)
1975	588
1976	610
1977	630
1978	654
1979	666
1980	692
1981	708
1982	712
1983	754
1984	748

a. Forecast the demand for the next five years using trend projection.

b. Calculated the mean absolute deviation and the mean squared error of this forecast for 1985-1989 given the following data.

Year	Demand (in 000s)
1985	762
1986	808
1987	786
1988	798
1989	826

Solution

a. We can use the year as the independent variable or a trend variable (x=1, 1975; x=10, 1984).

Year	x	y	xy	x^2
1975	1	588	588	1
1976	2	610	1220	4
1977	3	630	1890	9
1978	4	654	2616	16
1979	5	666	3330	25
1980	6	692	4152	36
1981	7	708	4956	49
1982	8	712	5696	64
1983	9	754	6786	81
1984	10	748	7480	100
	136	6540	56361	1496

The normal equations are:
$$6762 = 10b + 55m$$
$$38714 = 55b + 385m$$

Multiplying the first equation by 7 and subtracting the second from it (to eliminate m) gives:

$$47334 = 70b + 385m$$
$$38714 = 55b + 385m$$
$$8620 = 15b$$

$$b = 8620/15 = 574.67$$

181

Substituting this in the first equation and solving for m:
$$6762 = 10(574.67) + 55m$$

$$m = (6762-5746.7)/55 = 18.46$$

The trend line, therefore, is: $y = 574.67 + 18.46x$. To forecast years 1984-1989, simply extrapolate using this equation.

Year	x	Forecast
1985	11	$574.67 + 18.46(11) = 777.3$
1986	12	$574.67 + 18.46(12) = 796.2$
1987	13	$574.67 + 18.46(13) = 814.7$
1988	14	$574.67 + 18.46(14) = 833.1$
1989	15	$574.67 + 18.46(15) = 851.6$

b. The mean absolute deviation (MAD) is the average of the absolute values of the errors; the mean squared error (MSE) is the average of the squared values of the errors.

Year	Actual	Forecast	Error	Abs. Value of Error	Squared Error
1985	762	777.3	-15.7	15.7	247.5
1986	808	796.2	11.8	11.8	139.4
1987	786	814.7	-28.7	28.7	821.1
1988	798	833.1	-35.1	35.1	1233.1
1989	826	851.6	-25.6	25.6	654.1
				116.9	3095.2

$$\text{MAD} = 116.9/5 = 23.4, \quad \text{MSE} = 3095.2/5 = 619.0$$

REVIEW EXERCISES

The data in the following is to be used for Questions 1 through 9.

Year	Quarter	Sales
1981	1	393
	2	406
	3	400
	4	380
1982	1	391
	2	417
	3	412
	4	394
1983	1	403
	2	425
	3	409
	4	406
1984	1	422
	2	438
	3	427
	4	417

1. Use a four-quarter simple moving average model to find forecasted quarterly sales values for 1982-1984 (12 values in all are needed). Round all values to the nearest integer.

2. Use a simple exponential smoothing model with $\alpha = .40$ to give forecasts for the quarterly sales values for 1982-1984. Use a forecasted value for 1981, quarter 4 of 395. Round all values to the nearest integer.

3. Compare the two models in Questions 1 and 2 on the basis of their MAD values.

4. Use a tracking signal on the exponential smoothing model in Question 2. What does it suggest?

5. Use a trend-adjusted exponential smoothing model with $\alpha = .4$ and $\beta = .2$ to produce quarterly sales forecasts for 1982-1984. Assume an initial forecast of 395 for 1982, quarter 1. Round working values to the nearest tenth and the trend-adjusted forecast values to the nearest integer.

6. Compute the MAD for the model in Question 5, comparing the F' and A values over the time interval 1982, quarter 2, through 1984, quarter 4.

7. Fit a simple linear regression model to the example data, using the entire four years' worth.

8. Use the model developed in Question 7 to find predicted sales values for all 16 quarters in the interval 1981-1984.

*9 Using the predicted values from the regression equation found in Question 8 as a base, approximate multiplicative seasonal indexes for the four quarters.

CHAPTER TEST

1. Which of the following is <u>not</u> a <u>general</u> category of forecasting models as discussed in the text?
   a. Qualitative techniques.
   b. Trend extrapolation.
   c. Time-series analysis.
   d. Causal methods.

2. All quantitative forecasting techniques depend on:
   a. the use of a computer.
   b. a long planning horizon.
   c. the existence of adequate and accurate historical data.
   d. the identification of causal variables.

3. Which of the following was <u>not</u> identified as a qualitative technique?
   a. The Delphi method.
   b. Market research.
   c. Grass-roots forecasting.
   d. Econometric methods.

4. The time series component that refers to long-term growth or decay is:
   a. trend.
   b. cyclic.
   c. seasonal.
   d. erratic.

5. Given the values 51, 60, 47, 65, and 52 (in order), the four-period simple moving average forecast for period 6 is:
   a. 56.
   b. 52.
   c. 55.
   d. 55.75.

6. The forecast for period 1 is 100 and the actual value for period 1 is
   105. Using a simple exponential smoothing model with $\alpha = .2$, the forecast for period 2 is:
   a. 99.
   b. 104.
   c. 101.
   d. 100.2

7. Simple exponential smoothing models work best when forecasting:
   a. short range.
   b. medium range.
   c. long range.
   d. for several future periods.

8. The most common method of fitting a regression equation for trend projection is:
   a. eyeballing.
   b. minimizing MAD.
   c. minimizing the sum of errors.
   d. minimizing the sum of squared errors.

9. Which of the following is not generally considered a causal method of
   forecasting?
   a. Multiple regression models.
   b. Historical analogy.
   c. Simulation.
   d. Econometric models.

10. A tracking signal is used to identify forecasts that:
    a. ignore seasonality.
    b. are not properly accounting for cyclic effects.
    c. are not keeping pace with a trend.
    d. none of the above.

ANSWER KEY

Key Terms

1. H	5. J	9. B	13. Q	17. F
2. M	6. P	10. R	14. O	18. K
3. I	7. E	11. D	15. A	
4. C	8. N	12. G	16. L	

Review Problems

1.

Year	Qtr.	Sales	Forecast	Error	(For Q.3) |Error|
1981	1	393	–	–	–
	2	406	–	–	–
	3	400	–	–	–
	4	380	–	–	–
1982	1	391	395	–4	4
	2	417	394	23	23
	3	412	397	15	15
	4	394	400	–6	6
1983	1	403	404	–1	1
	2	425	407	18	18
	3	409	409	0	0
	4	406	408	–2	2
1984	1	422	411	11	11
	2	438	416	22	22
	3	427	419	8	8
	4	417	423	–6	6

$$\sum |\text{Error}| = 116$$

$$\text{MAD} = 116/12 = 9.67$$

2.

Year	Qtr.	Sales	Forecast	Error	(For Q.3) |Error|
1982	1	391	395	–4	4
	2	417	393	24	24
	3	412	403	9	9
	4	394	407	–13	13
1983	1	403	402	1	1
	2	425	402	23	23
	3	409	411	–2	2
	4	406	410	–4	4
1984	1	422	408	14	14
	2	438	414	24	24
	3	427	424	3	3
	4	417	425	–8	8

$$\sum |\text{Error}| = 129$$

$$\text{MAD} = 116/12 = 10.75$$

3. The calculations of MAD values for the two models are shown in the answers for Questions 1 and 2. The MAD for the simple moving average model is 9.67 as compared to the MAD for the simple exponential smoothing model of 10.75. The simple moving average model appears to fit the data better.

4. The tracking signal is found by dividing the running sum of forecast errors (RSFE) for a period by the MAD for that period. The Error and Absolute Error columns from Question 2 are repeated in the table below along with the RSFE, MAD, and Tracking Signal (TS) values for each period.

185

Year	Qtr.	Error	RSFE	|Error|	MAD	TS
1982	1	-4	-4	4	4.00	-1.0
	2	24	20	24	14.00	1.4
	3	9	29	9	12.33	2.4
	4	-13	16	13	12.50	1.3
1983	1	1	17	1	10.20	1.7
	2	23	40	23	12.33	3.2
	3	-2	38	2	10.86	3.5
	4	-4	34	4	10.00	3.4
1984	1	14	48	14	10.44	4.6
	2	24	72	24	11.80	6.1
	3	3	75	3	11.00	6.8
	4	8	83	8	10.75	7.7

It should be apparent that the forecasts are lagging behind the actual values. The tracking signal is growing more and more positive. This suggests that a trend model would be more appropriate.

To recap from the text, the procedure is as follows:

i) Compute a simple forecast for period t:
$$F_t = F_{t-1} + \alpha (A_{t-1} - F_{t-1})$$

ii) Compute the trend value t_t:
$$t_t = F_t - F_{t-1}$$

iii) Calculate the exponentially smoothed trend T_t:
$$T_t = T_{t-1} + \beta (t_t - T_{t-1})$$

iv) Calculate the trend-adjusted forecast F'_t
$$F'_t = F_t + \frac{1-\beta}{\beta} T_t$$

Applying this procedure to the data given, we have:

Year	Qtr.	A	F	t	T	F'	(For Q.6) Error	|Error|
1982	1	391	395.0	-	0	-	-	-
	2	471	393.4	-1.6	-.3	392	25	25
	3	412	402.8	9.4	1.6	409	3	3
	4	394	406.5	3.7	2.0	415	-21	21
1983	1	403	402.0	-4.5	.7	405	-2	2
	2	425	402.4	.4	.6	405	20	20
	3	409	411.4	9.0	2.3	421	-12	12
	4	406	410.4	-1.0	1.6	417	-11	11
1984	1	422	408.6	-1.8	.9	412	10	10
	2	438	414.0	5.4	1.8	421	17	17
	3	427	423.6	9.6	3.4	437	-10	10
	4	417	425.0	1.4	3.0	437	-20	20

$$\sum |Error| = 151$$

$$MAD = 151/11 = 13.72$$

6. As can be seen from the two right-hand columns in the table in the answer to Question 5, the MAD for the trend-adjusted model is 13.72. Although this is higher than the MAD for the simple exponentially smoothed model,

the model does, in a sense, fit the data better. The actual errors fluctuate in sign, with positive and negative errors interspersed.

This suggests that the model is, in fact, following the trend and that the errors are due to something else, possibly seasonality.

7. We let y be the actual sales and x be time periods, counting with 1981, quarter 1 being x = 1.

Year	Qtr.	x	y	xy	x^2	(Q.8) Y
1981	1	1	393	393	1	391.7
	2	2	406	812	4	394.0
	3	3	400	1200	9	396.3
	4	4	380	1520	16	398.5
1982	1	5	391	1955	25	400.8
	2	6	417	2502	36	403.1
	3	7	412	2884	49	405.3
	4	8	394	3152	64	407.6
1983	1	9	403	3627	81	409.9
	2	10	425	4250	100	412.2
	3	11	409	4499	121	414.4
	4	12	406	4872	144	416.7
1984	1	13	422	5486	169	419.0
	2	14	438	6132	196	421.2
	3	15	427	6405	225	423.5
	4	16	417	6672	256	425.8
	Totals	136	6540	56361	1496	

The normal equations are: $6540 = 16b + 136m$
$$56361 = 13b + 1496m$$

This is solved to give: b = 389.475
m = 2.26765

8. The predicted value for sales, Y_i, is found by substituting the appropriate x for the period, x_i, into the equation $Y_i = 389.475 + 2.26765x_i$. The resulting values are shown in the right-hand column of the table in the answer to Question 7.

9. The seasonal indexes can be approximated by averaging the ratios y_i/Y_i for the four repetitions (1981-1984) of each quarter.

Value of y/Y

Quarter	1981	1982	1983	1984	Average
1	1.003	.976	.983	1.007	.992
2	1.030	1.034	1.031	1.040	1.034
3	1.009	1.017	.987	1.008	1.005
4	.954	.967	.974	.979	.969

The seasonal indexes are found in the right-hand column of the table.

Chapter Test

1. b	3. d	5. a	7. a	9. b
2. c	4. a	6. c	8. d	10. c

CHAPTER FOURTEEN

QUEUING MODELS

MAIN POINTS

1. Queuing theory is a branch of applied probability that involves the description of systems that contain waiting lines.

2. Queuing theory can be applied, if certain situational characteristics are met, to make decisions about the structure and operation of a queuing system.

3. Decisions that can be made include: the number of servers to use, the speed of a server, the number of waiting spaces to provide, the queue discipline to follow, and the number of calling population members to assign to a single server.

4. Queuing models are not optimization models but are descriptive. Using a queuing model for optimization involves searching among the possible decision alternatives, using the model to evaluate the quality of each alternative considered. Unlike linear programming, there is no guarantee that the optimal decision will necessarily be considered.

5. Queuing systems have four parts: the calling population, the queue, the service facility, and the served calling units.

6. The most important characteristics of a calling population are its size, the pattern of arrivals, and the attitude of the calling units.

7. The population size can be finite or infinite. Although almost all populations are really finite (although many are very large), a population will be considered infinite unless the probability of an arrival is significantly changed when one or more members of the population are in the queue or are receiving service. Infinite population models are generally easier to analyze theoretically.

8. Calling units arrive for service according to a predetermined schedule or at random. Analytic models usually are applied to random arrivals. If arrivals are random, it is necessary to determine the probability distribution of the time between consecutive arrivals. A common distribution for interarrival times is the exponential, in which case the number of arrivals in a time interval has a Poisson distribution.

9. Calling unit attitude refers to the willingness of an arrival to wait for service. A potential customer who refuses to join a queue balks. One who initially joins the queue but leaves before receiving service reneges.

10. A queue may have a limited or unlimited potential length.

11. The three basic properties of the service facility are its structure, the distribution of service times, and the service discipline.

12. Service facilities may be single- or multichannel. Multichannel is also called parallel servers. A service channel may be single- or multiphase. In a single-phase channel, one server does all the work. In a multiphase channel, the work is divided among several specialized servers, each of which does a portion. A multiphase system may be viewed as a series of single-phase systems, with the output from one phase becoming the input of the next.

13. Service times can be constant or random. If random, a probability distribution for the length of service is needed. In many cases, this is an exponential distribution.

14. The service discipline determines which waiting customer receives service next. The possibilities are first come, first served (FCFS), also called first in, first out (FIFO), priority, and random. Most human situations (unless life-threatening) are FCFS because it is considered fair. Priority systems may be more efficient if costs are involved. They can be preemptive (an arriving customer with higher priority interrupts the existing lower priority service) or nonpreemptive (the arrival waits until the present service is completed).

15. There are two types of phases in the life of a queuing system: transient and steady state. In its transient phases, the system is in a state of change, with line lengths and waiting times either growing or shrinking. In steady state, the system characteristics fluctuate around stable average values. Transient states occur whenever there are major changes in the system, such as when a new server is added or the customer arrival rate changes. Most analysis is of steady-state behavior.

16. A wide variety of analytic queuing models exist. The formulas for the more popular system performance measures under steady-state conditions have been developed mathematically on the basis of assumptions about system probability distributions, structure, and operating rules.

17. For more complex queuing systems, it is necessary to use simulation models. While more versatile, they are much more expensive and time-consuming to develop and use. In addition, they are subject to the experimental error of any statistical sampling procedure.

18. Two approaches to designing queuing systems are design to minimize total costs and design to minimize the cost of meeting performance standards.

19. The two basic kinds of costs in a queuing system are the cost of providing service and the cost of waiting. A system design that gives a low cost for one tends to give a high cost for the other. When both costs are measurable, the appropriate design criterion is to minimize their sum.

20. The cost of waiting is not always readily measurable. In this case, the usual practice is to establish a desired performance level on some criterion, such as waiting time or queue length, and to minimize the server cost of meeting it.

21. While most smaller analytic queuing models can be solved by hand or with a calculator, large scale analytic models and simulation studies need to be done on a computer, especially if a large number of possible system configurations are to be compared.

SUGGESTED READINGS

Selected applications are:

Chelst, K., "A Coal Unloader: a Finite Queuing System with Breakdowns," Interfaces, v. 11, n. 5 (October 1981), pp. 12-25.

Gilliam, R. R., "A Application of Queuing Theory to Airport Passenger Security Screening," Interfaces, v. 9, n. 4 (August 1979), pp. 117-123.

Siegel, S., "The Value of Queuing Theory: a Case Study," Interfaces, v. 9, n. 5 (October 1979), pp. 148-151.

Sze, D. Y., "A Queuing Model for Telephone Operator Staffing," Operations Research, v. 32, n. 2 (March/April 1984), pp. 229-249.

Vogel, M. A., "Queuing Theory Applied to Machine Manning," Interfaces, v. 9, n. 4 (August 1979), pp. 1-8.

KEY TERMS

Match each term with the correct definition below.

Terms

_____ 1. attitude

_____ 2. calling unit

_____ 3. FCFS

_____ 4. input source

_____ 5. multichannel

_____ 6. multiphase

_____ 7. Poisson process

_____ 8. preemptive priority

_____ 9. queue discipline

_____ 10. queuing system

_____ 11. random arrivals

_____ 12. service facility

_____ 13. steady state

_____ 14. transient

Definitions

A. A service facility in which the service operation is divided into distinct parts, each of which is performed by a different server.

B. A queue discipline in which an arriving customer with higher priority interrupts the service being provided to a customer with lower priority.

C. Characterizes a queuing system for which the performance measures have stabilized.

191

D. Reaction of a calling unit to having to wait for service.

E. A service system that includes a waiting line.

F. A customer or potential customer requiring service.

G. Calling units that do not arrive on a schedule.

H. A service system with more than one identical server.

I. The phase of a queuing system's life characterized by growth or decay of line lengths and waiting times.

J. The collection of potential customers for a service facility.

K. The rule that determines which waiting customer gets served next.

L. Characterizes the situation in which interarrival times are exponentially distributed.

M. A queue discipline in which the earliest arrival receives service first.

N. The part of a queuing system that provides service.

SOLVED PROBLEM

Between the hours of one and three in the afternoon, customers arrive at the Central National Bank office at an average rate of two per minute, Poisson distributed. It takes a teller an average of 45 seconds to process a single customer, the service time following an exponential distribution. How many tellers are required to have an average time in line (before service) of no more than 30 seconds per customer?

<u>Solution</u>

This situation satisfies the assumptions of a multiserver model with Poisson arrivals and exponential service times. The arrival rate (λ) is 2 per minute and the service time is 45 seconds per customer. It is necessary to express the service as a rate (and consistent time units) so the service rate (μ) is

$$\frac{60 \text{ seconds/minute}}{45 \text{ seconds/customer}} = 4/3 \text{ per minute}$$

The service standard is expressed in terms of the average time in line so we will need to calculate W_q for each value of s that we evaluate. For $s\mu$ to be greater than λ, we need $s \geq 2$, so we will evaluate 2 servers or more.

To find W_q, we will need the following information:

P(0), from the table in Appendix H of the text

$$L_q = \frac{P(0)(\lambda/\mu)^s \rho}{s!(1-\rho)^2}$$

$$W_q = L_q/\lambda$$

192

We start with s = 2, which gives $\lambda/s\mu$ = .75.

P(0) = .1429 by interpolation

$$L_q = \frac{(.1429)(1.5)^2(.75)}{2!(.25)^2} = 1.929$$

W_q = 1.929/2 = .965 minutes

Since .965 is greater than the allowable average waiting time of .5 minutes, s = 2 is not large enough. Therefore, try s = 3, for which $\lambda/s\mu$ = .50.

P(0) = .2105

$$L_q = \frac{(.2105)(1.5)^3(.50)}{3!(.5)^2} = .237$$

W_q = .237/2 = .118 minutes

Since .118 is less than the allowable average waiting time of .5 minutes, three tellers is sufficient.

REVIEW EXERCISES

1. For a single-server, infinite population, unlimited queue, FCFS queuing system with no balking or reneging, the calling units arrive according to a Poisson process with an average time between arrivals of 10 minutes. Service time is exponentially distributed with an average time of 6 minutes.

   a. What fraction of the time is the server busy?
   b. What is the average number waiting in line?
   c. What is the average time spent in the system?

2. Local Airlines has a single reservation clerk on telephone duty. The phone has several lines coming into it. If the first line is busy, the call will automatically be rolled up the list of numbers until it finds a vacant line if there is one. Then an automatic answering device takes over, informing the caller that he or she will be taken care of in turn. Callers who get this message wait. If all available lines are full with waiting callers, the incoming call gets a busy signal. In this case, the caller will go to another airline.

   Calls follow a Poisson process, averaging one per five minutes. To handle a call takes an average of two minutes, following an exponential service time distribution. If there are four lines on the phone, what percentage of calls are turned away because all the lines are busy?

3. The Benelux Manufacturing Co. uses a large number of identical machines for one part of its manufacturing process. These machines carry out their operation automatically. However, they occasionally jam up. This happens on an average of once every five minutes per machine, following a Poisson process. Clearing a jammed machine is usually fast, taking an average of 30 seconds, exponentially distributed.

The machines are to be grouped into small areas with one operator responsible for all the machines in an area. If there are five machines in an area, what is the average number of machines not in production (jammed and either being cleared or waiting) at any moment?

*4. (Continuation of (3).) Assume that an operating machine makes a net contribution to profit and overhead of $50 per hour and that the cost of an operator is $12 per hour, including fringe benefits. How many machines should an operator be responsible for?

5. Vern's Bug Shop specializes in tuning up Volkswagens. It takes Vern an average of 45 minutes to do a complete tune-up, with a standard deviation of 5 minutes. Tune-up time is approximately Normally distributed. An average of 9 cars per 8 hour day come for tune-ups, Poisson distributed.

How many cars, on average are waiting for a tune-up? On average, how long will an arriving car spend at Vern's?

CHAPTER TEST

1. Which of the following are basic components of a queuing system?
   a. Service facility.
   b. Arrival rate.
   c. Service time distribution.
   d. Queue discipline.

2. The <u>attitude</u> of a calling unit refers to:
   a. how pleasant it is.
   b. how frequently they arrive.
   c. whether it will wait for service.
   d. how long service will take.

3. Whether a calling population is considered finite or infinite depends on:
   a. how frequently units arrive at the service facility.
   b. whether the fact that a unit is receiving or waiting for service affects the arrival rate.
   c. whether the arrivals can be counted.
   d. none of the above.

4. If arrivals are random, that means that they follow a Poisson process.
   a. True
   b. False

5. Which of the following is <u>not</u> a basic property of the service facility?
   a. Structure.
   b. Service time distribution.
   c. Service discipline.
   d. Calling unit attitude.

6. If service on a unit will be interrupted by the arrival of a higher priority unit, the service discipline is called:
   a. preemptive priority.
   b. nonpreemptive priority.
   c. random.
   d. dedicated.

7. Which of the following is <u>not</u> a characteristic of the basic single-server model?
   a. Poisson arrivals.
   b. FCFS service discipline.
   c. Limited queue.
   d. Exponential service time.

8. In most queuing systems, which of the following would <u>not</u> generally be considered a controllable feature?
   a. Number of servers.
   b. Rate of service.
   c. Allowable queue length.
   d. Calling unit arrival rate.

9. The arrival time distribution used in most queuing models is:
   a. exponential.
   b. Normal.
   c. arbitrary.
   d. constant.

10. The economic analysis of queuing systems involves consideration of:
    a. waiting cost.
    b. service cost.
    c. both of the above.
    d. none of the above.

ANSWER KEY

<u>Terms</u>

1. D	4. J	7. L	10. E	13. C
2. F	5. H	8. B	11. G	14. I
3. M	6. A	9. K	12. N	

<u>Review Exercises</u>

1. Average interarrival time = 10 minutes gives λ = 6 per hour. Average service time = 6 minutes gives μ = 10 per hour. Using the basic single-server model:

a. $\rho = \lambda/\mu = 6/10 = 60$ percent of the time

b. $L_q = \lambda^2/[\mu(\mu - \lambda)] = 36/[10(10 - 6)] = 36/40 = .90$ customers

c. $W_s = 1/(\mu - \lambda) = 1/(10 - 6) = 1/4$ hour = 15 minutes

2. Use the single-server model with a finite queue.

   λ = .2 per minute, μ = .5 per minute, M = 4

$$P(0) = \frac{1 - (\lambda/\mu)}{1 - (\lambda/\mu)^{M+1}} = \frac{1 - (.2/.5)}{1 - (.2/.5)^5} = \frac{1 - .4}{1 - .01024} = .6062$$

$$P(n) = P(0)(\lambda/\mu)^n$$

$$P(4) = (.6062)(.2/.5)^4 = .0155$$

Approximately 1.55 percent of the incoming calls are rejected because the lines are all busy.

3. Use the finite population model.

$\lambda = .2$ per minute, $\mu = 2.0$ per minute, $N = 5$, $s = 1$

Since $s = 1$, the equations for $P(n)$ are:

$$P(0) = \frac{1}{1 + \sum_{n-1}^{N} \frac{N!}{(N-n)!}(\lambda/\mu)^n}$$

$$P(n) = P(0)\frac{N!}{(N-n)!}(\lambda/\mu)^n \qquad \text{for } 1 \leq n \leq N$$

$$P(0) = \frac{1}{1 + [\frac{5!}{4!}(.1) + \frac{5!}{3!}(.1)^2 + \frac{5!}{2!}(.1)^3 + \frac{5!}{1!}(.1)^4 + \frac{5!}{0!}(.1)^5]}$$

$$= \frac{1}{1 + [.5 + .2 + .06 + .012 + .0012]} = \frac{1}{1.7732} = .564$$

$$P(1) = (.564)(5!/4!)(.1)^1 = .282$$

$$P(2) = (.564)(5!/3!)(.1)^2 = .113$$

$$P(3) = (.564)(5!/2!)(.1)^3 = .034$$

$$P(4) = (.564)(5!/1!)(.1)^4 = .007$$

$$P(5) = (.564)(5!/0!)(.1)^5 = .0007$$

$$L_s = \sum_{n=1}^{N} nP(n)$$

$$= (1)(.282) + (2)(.113) + (3)(.034) + (4)(.007) + (5)(.0007)$$

$$= .642 \text{ machines out of service at any point in time}$$

4. Since there is a large number of machines, it is reasonable to find the value of N, the number of machines to assign to a single operator, that will minimize the combined operator and lost profit contribution per hour machine. The total cost per hour of a system with N machines and one operator is:

$$TC(N) \; 12 + 50L_s$$

so the average cost per hour per machine is:

$$AC(N) = \frac{TC(N)}{N} = \frac{12 + 50L_s}{N}$$

With N = 5 this is:

$$AC(5) = \frac{12 + 50(.642)}{5} = \frac{44.1}{5} = 8.82.$$

Next try N = 6.

$$P(0) = \frac{1}{1 + [\frac{6!}{5!}(.1) + \frac{6!}{4!}(.1)^2 + \frac{6!}{3!}(.1)^3 + \frac{6!}{2!}(.1)^4 + \frac{6!}{1!}(.1)^5 + \frac{6!}{0!}(.1)^6]}$$

$$= \frac{1}{1 + [.6 + .3 + .12 + .036 + .0072 + .00072]} = \frac{1}{2.06392} = 0.4845$$

$$P(1) = (.4845)(6!/5!)(.1)^1 = .291$$

$$P(2) = (.4845)(6!/4!)(.1)^2 = .145$$

$$P(3) = (.4845)(6!/3!)(.1)^3 = .058$$

$$P(4) = (.4845)(6!/2!)(.1)^4 = .017$$

$$P(5) = (.4845)(6!/1!)(.1)^5 = .003$$

$$P(6) = (.4845)(6!/0!)(.1)^6 = .0003$$

$$L_s = (1)(.291)+(2)(.145)+(3)(.058)+(4)(.017)+(5)(.003)+(6)(.0003)$$
$$= .840$$

$$AC(6) = \frac{12 + 50(.840)}{6} = 9.00$$

Since $AC(6) > AC(5)$, we want $N \leq 5$. We next try N = 4.

$$P(0) = \frac{1}{1 + [\frac{4!}{3!}(.1) + \frac{4!}{2!}(.1)^2 + \frac{4!}{1!}(.1)^3 + \frac{4!}{0!}(.1)^4]}$$

$$= \frac{1}{1 + [.4 + .12 + .024 + .0024]} = \frac{1}{1.5464} = .647$$

$$P(1) = (.647)(4!/3!)(.1)^1 = .259$$

$$P(2) = (.647)(4!/2!)(.1)^2 = .078$$

$$P(3) = (.647)(4!/1!)(.1)^3 = .016$$

$$P(4) = (.647)(4!/0!)(.1)^4 = .0016$$

$$L_s = (1)(.259) + (2)(.078) + (3)(.016) + (4)(.0016) = .469$$

$$AC(4) = \frac{12 + 50(.469)}{4} = 8.86.$$

Since $AC(4) > AC(5) < AC(6)$, the optimal value for N is 5. Assign five machines to each worker.

5. Use a single-server model with arbitrary service times.

λ = 1.125 per hour, μ = 4/3 per hour, σ^2 = .00694 hour^2, ρ = .84375

$$L_q = (\lambda^2 \sigma^2 + \rho^2)/[2(1 - \rho)]$$

$$= [(1.125)^2(.00694) + (.84375)^2]/[2(.15625)] = 2.31$$

The average number of cars waiting to be tuned up is 2.31.

$$W_s = W_q + (1/\mu) = L_q/\lambda + (1/\mu)$$

$$= (2.31/1.125) + .75 = 2.80 \text{ hours}$$

A car spends an average of 2.80 hours at the shop.

Chapter Test

1. a   3. b   5. d   7. c   9. a
2. c   4. b   6. a   8. d   10. c

CHAPTER FIFTEEN

DISCRETE DIGITAL SIMULATION

MAIN POINTS

1. Because of its flexibility and its ability to be used where no other technique can, simulation is the most widely used management science technique.

2. Discrete digital simulation, often referred to as Monte Carlo simulation, is a descriptive technique rather than an optimization procedure.

3. Simulation involves performing experiments on a model of a system.

4. A simulation model plays much the same role for a management scientist that a laboratory plays for a physical scientist.

5. By changing parameters and structures in a simulation model, the analyst can infer how different system configurations will behave under various conditions.

6. Simulation is used because it is impossible or impractical to experiment on the real system or because the system is too complex to model and solve analytically.

7. Applications of simulation models appear in the literature from practically all areas, at all levels of decision making.

8. Virtually all realistic simulation applications require computer implementation because of the large amounts of computation.

9. To execute a probabilistic simulation requires the ability to generate values for the stochastic variables in the system. This is done by randomly selecting numbers from a uniform distribution on the range 0 to 1 and then converting those numbers into values from the desired probability distribution with a process generator.

10. Many process generators work by inverting the cumulative probability distribution of the variable of interest, solving for the random variable value whose cumulative probability is equal to the random number selected.

11. The basic steps in a simulation study are problem formulation, data collection and analysis, model formulation, program generation, validation of the model and program, experimental design, and output analysis.

12. Problem formulation requires developing an explicit statement of the objectives of the study and identifying the criteria for evaluating the results. Objectives are questions to be answered, hypotheses to be tested, or effects to be estimated.

13. Data is required for describing the system, developing probability distributions, and testing the model's validity.

14. Based on the data, probability distributions and parameters are hypothesized and tested using goodness-of-fit tests such as the Chi-square and Kolmogorov-Smirnov tests.

15. The model developed must balance realism and cost.

16. The model is translated into a computer program written in either a compiler language, like FORTRAN or BASIC, or one of the special-purpose simulation languages, like SIMSCRIPT, SLAM II, or GPSS.

17. The special simulation languages simplify the programming and increase the probability of generating a valid program. Their limited use is due to lack of knowledge of these languages by analysts.

18. Model and program validation involve testing that the program is an accurate translation of the model, that the process generators produce values with the same distributions as in the real system, and that the outputs of the model are reasonable when viewed subjectively and (if possible) historically.

19. Experimental design involves using standard statistical concepts to determine what variable combinations to run through the model. The results of these runs can be tested and interpreted using standard statistical techniques.

20. A deterministic simulation involves no random variables. Combinations of parameters are run through the model to predict what system behavior will be under various scenarios. They are common in finance.

21. Simulation should not, in general, be used if an analytic technique is available. A simulation should only be used if its cost is less than its benefits.

22. Simulation is advantageous when the model is too complex to solve and the real system is impossible or impractical to experiment on. Dynamic behavior can be modelled. Time can be compressed.

23. The disadvantages of simulation are that it is expensive, is not an optimization technique, and is subject to sampling error.

24. The application of simulation has been and continues to be increased due to developments in computer hardware and software. Specific developments include the decreased cost of computing, the increase in corporate data bases, and improvements in simulation languages.

SUGGESTED READINGS

A discussion of several applications of simulation can be found in:

Pritsker, A. A. B., Introduction to Simulation and SLAM II, (New York: Halsted Press, 1986), Chapter 4.

Other selected applications are:

Bar-Lev, D. and M. A. Pollatschek, "Simulation as an Aid in Decision Making at Israel Fertilizers and Chemicals," Interfaces, v. 11, n. 2 (April 1981), pp. 17-21.

Farina, R., G. A. Kochenberger, and T. Obremski, "The Computer Runs the Bolder Boulder: A Simulation of a Major Running Race," Interfaces, v. 19, n. 2 (March-April 1989), pp. 48-55.

Harris, C. M., K. L. Hoffman, and P. B. Saunders, "Modeling the IRS Telephone Taxpayer Information System," Operations Research, v. 35, n. 4 (July-August 1987), pp. 504-523.

Kern, G. M., "A Computer Simulation Model for the Study of Police Patrol Deployment," Simulation, v. 52, n. 6 (June 1989), pp. 226-232.

Landauer, E. G. and L. C. Becker, "Reducing Waiting Time at Security Checkpoints," Interfaces, v. 19, n. 5 (September-October 1989), pp. 57-65.

Macon, M. R. and E. Turban, "Energy Audit Program Simulation," Interfaces, v. 11, n. 1 (February 1981), pp. 13-19.

Riccio, L. J. and A. Litke, "Making a Clean Sweep: Simulating the Effects of Illegally Parked Cars on New York City's Mechanical Street-Cleaning Efforts," Operations Research, v. 34, n. 5 (September-October 1986), pp. 661-666.

Thinnes, K. M. and V. Kachitvichyanukul, "Simulation of Printed Circuit-Board Manufacturing," Journal of the Operational Research Society, v. 40, n. 7 (July 1989), pp. 643-647.

KEY TERMS

Match each term with the correct definition from below.

Terms

_____ 1. cumulative distribution   _____ 6. model validation

_____ 2. deterministic simulation   _____ 7. Monte Carlo simulation

_____ 3. experimental design   _____ 8. process generator

_____ 4. goodness-of-fit test   _____ 9. random number

_____ 5. GPSS   _____ 10. stochastic variable

Definitions

A. A special-purpose simulation language.

B. A function that turns a random number into the value of a random variable from a specified probability distribution.

201

C. A variable whose value is determined by a probability distribution.

D. A function that shows the probability that a random variable is less than or equal to a specific value.

E. A number selected from the uniform distribution in the range 0 to 1.

F. The determination of what combinations of system features and parameter values to test with a simulation.

G. Checking to see that a model is a reasonable representation of the system it is supposed to describe.

H. A statistical procedure for checking that a hypothesized probability distribution could reasonably have generated a particular data set.

I. A simulation with no random variables.

J. Another term for a discrete digital simulation involving probability distributions.

SOLVED PROBLEM

The local drugstore stocks copies of the Sunday newspaper from a nearby city. The papers cost the store 85 cents and sell for $1.25. Leftover papers have no value. Each week the store places an order for the following Sunday. They are trying to decide on a good ordering policy. Two have been suggested:

    Rule I: Order the previous week's demand.
    Rule II: Order an amount equal to the average plus
                one standard deviation of weekly demand.

Based on their records of past weekly sales and unfilled requests, the store estimates the following weekly demand distribution:

d	p(d)
10	.10
11	.20
12	.30
13	.20
14	.15
15	.05

Use a simulation model to determine which of the two rules to use. Simulate for 20 weeks. The demand last week was for 14 papers. Use the second column of Table 15.6 for the random numbers.

Solution

Assuming that there is no penalty cost associated with a lost sale, the appropriate way to compare the rules is on the basis of average weekly profit. The profit for a week is:

Profit = Revenue - Cost
      = 1.25(Sales) - .85(Stock)
      = 1.25 min(d,q) - .85q

where d = weekly demand and q = stocking quantity.

The process generator for the probability distribution can be found by using the ranges derived from the cumulative probability distribution, P(d):

d	p(d)	P(d)	Random Numbers (r)
10	.10	.10	0 - .099999
11	.20	.30	.10 - .299999
12	.30	.60	.30 - .599999
13	.20	.80	.60 - .799999
14	.15	.95	.80 - .949999
15	.05	1.00	.95 - .999999

Based on the probability distribution, we find that the mean and standard deviation of weekly demands are 12.25 and 1.34, respectively, so the mean plus one standard deviation is 13.59, which we will round up to 14. The two tables show the simulations for the two rules. Notice that the same random numbers have been used for both simulations. This is called correlated sampling and is a common procedure in using simulation to compare alternative configurations of a system. It increases the accuracy of estimation of the difference between two random variables. The concept is the same as that in the paired comparison t-test in statistics.

Simulation Using Rule I

Week	q	r	d	Profit	Cumulative Profit
1	14	.353333	12	3.10	3.10
2	12	.441906	12	4.80	7.90
3	12	.579120	12	4.80	12.70
4	12	.992685	15	4.80	17.50
5	15	.664736	13	3.50	21.00
6	13	.447204	12	3.95	24.95
7	12	.436322	12	4.80	29.75
8	12	.522334	12	4.80	34.55
9	12	.319852	12	4.80	39.35
10	12	.722047	13	4.80	44.15
11	13	.155976	11	2.70	46.85
12	11	.680668	13	4.40	51.25
13	13	.806714	14	5.20	56.45
14	14	.876081	14	5.60	62.05
15	14	.984704	15	5.60	67.65
16	15	.205187	11	1.00	68.65
17	11	.165323	11	4.40	73.05
18	11	.800478	14	4.40	77.45
19	14	.434235	12	3.10	80.55
20	12	.620655	13	4.80	85.35

Average weekly profit = 85.35/20 = 4.2675

Simulation Using Rule II

Week	q	r	d	Profit	Cumulative Profit
1	14	.353333	12	3.10	3.10
2	14	.441906	12	3.10	6.20
3	14	.579120	12	3.10	9.30
4	14	.992685	15	5.60	14.90
5	14	.664736	13	4.35	19.25
6	14	.447204	12	3.10	22.35
7	14	.436322	12	3.10	25.45
8	14	.522334	12	3.10	28.55
9	14	.319852	12	3.10	31.65
10	14	.722047	13	4.35	36.00
11	14	.155976	11	1.85	37.85
12	14	.680668	13	4.35	42.20
13	14	.806714	14	5.60	47.80
14	14	.876081	14	5.60	53.40
15	14	.984704	15	5.60	59.00
16	14	.205187	11	1.85	60.85
17	14	.165323	11	1.85	62.70
18	14	.800478	14	5.60	68.30
19	14	.434235	12	3.10	71.40
20	14	.620655	13	4.35	75.75

Average weekly profit = 75.75/20 = 3.7875

Based on the results on the simulation, Rule I (order the previous week's demand) appears to be preferable.

REVIEW EXERCISES

1. Using the first column of random numbers from Table 15.6, draw a sample of size 10 from the following probability distribution.

x	p(x)
0	.05
1	.10
2	.20
3	.25
4	.20
5	.10
6	.10

2. Customers arrive at a gas station according to a Poisson process with mean arrival rate 20 per hour. Use the first 9 random numbers in the second column of Table 15.6 to determine the times of arrivals of 10 consecutive cars, assuming the first car arrives at 9:00 a.m. Round your times off to the nearest minute.

3. Cars arrive at a self-service, one-stall automatic car wash according to the interarrival time probability distribution on the next page. The car wash takes exactly two minutes to wash a car. Simulate the operation of the car wash for 10 arrivals, assuming that the first arrives at time 0 to find an empty facility with no queue. Estimate the percentage of utilization and the average waiting time.

Δt (minutes)	$p(\Delta t)$
1	.15
2	.30
3	.40
4	.15

Use the first column in Table 15.6 for random numbers.

*4. Customers arrive at the drive-in window of a bank on an average of one every two minutes, arrivals following a Poisson distribution. Service takes an average of 1.5 minutes, following an exponential distribution. An arriving customer will wait, regardless of the length of the line. There is no limit to how long the line may become.

a. Simulate the operation of this queuing system for 20 arrivals. Start with the following conditions: There is a customer at the window who starts service at time 0. There is an arrival at time 0 (not one of the 20). There is one additional customer waiting when this arrival takes place. Find the average waiting time of the 20 arrivals. Carry all times to the nearest one-tenth of a minute. Use the random numbers from column 3 of Table 15.6 for arrivals and the numbers from column 4 for service times.

b. Compare your results with the theoretical results from queuing theory.

5. The fire department uses a special chemical for certain kinds of fires. This chemical is bought from a distant supplier, so the delivery time is uncertain. The weekly use is also uncertain. Probability distributions have been developed for both on the basis of past use and delivery times.

Delivery Time Probability Distribution:

Delivery Time (weeks)	Probability
1	.20
2	.40
3	.25
4	.15

Weekly Use: x has a Normal distribution with $\mu = 1000$ and $\sigma = 100$, both measured in pounds.

a. Using simulation, estimate the mean and standard deviation of delivery-time use. Assume use from week-to-week is independent. Round the weekly use amounts to the nearest pound. Use columns 5 and 6 of Table 15.6 for the delivery time and weekly use random numbers, respectively. Use ten delivery periods for the sample.

*b. Develop and run a computer program to perform the simulation for 1000 deliveries. Test whether the delivery time use can be assumed to have a Normal probability distribution.

*6. A machine has three identical circuits in it. In order for the machine to operate, all three must be functioning. The probability distribution for the life (or time to failure) of a circuit is exponential with a mean of 2500 hours. If a circuit fails it takes one hour to open and close the machine and an additional hour to replace the circuit. If more than one circuit is replaced simultaneously it takes a total of one hour plus one hour for each circuit. (To replace one circuit takes two hours; to replace two circuits takes three hours; to replace three circuits takes four hours.) A circuit costs $15. It costs $50 per hour in repairman time, operator idle time, and lost profit contribution to have the machine out of operation.

Three maintenance policies are being considered:
   i) Replace each circuit as it fails;
  ii) Replace the failed circuit plus any others 2500 or more hours old;
 iii) Replace all circuits if any one fails.

Simulate the operation of the machine for 15,000 hours. Use columns 1, 2, and 3 from Table 15.6 for the three circuits. Assume that all three circuits are new at the start. Due to the big difference between failure times and repair times, do not worry about extending the life of a circuit while another is being replaced. Round times to the nearest hour.

CHAPTER TEST

1. Simulation is used more often than any other management science because it:
    a. is inexpensive.
    b. guarantees an optimal solution.
    c. is flexible.
    d. all of the above.

2. Another name for discrete digital simulation is:
    a. Monte Carlo simulation.
    b. deterministic simulation.
    c. process generation.
    d. random number inversion.

3. A function that relates a uniformly distributed random number to a random variable with some specified distribution is called:
    a. a random number generator.
    b. a process generator.
    c. a cumulative distribution.
    d. a probability function.

4. Which of the following is a possible objective of a simulation study?
    a. A comparison of system configurations.
    b. A hypothesis test.
    c. The estimation of an effect.
    d. All are.

5. Which of the following tests can be used for testing the goodness-of-fit of a probability distribution to a data set?
    a. t test.
    b. Analysis of variance.
    c. Chi-square.
    d. Fischer's F.

6. Model building involves balancing the model's realism against:
   a. data requirements.
   b. programming cost.
   c. cost of execution.
   d. all of the above.

7. Model validation should involve:
   a. program testing.
   b. variable generation tests.
   c. subjective validation.
   d. all of the above.

8. A simulation is called deterministic if:
   a. we know what we want to study.
   b. all the probability distributions are known.
   c. it has no random variables.
   d. it can be solved analytically.

9. Which of the following is not an advantage of simulation?
   a. It permits the modelling of complex and dynamic phenomena.
   b. The computer programs can be written by anyone.
   c. It allows time compression.
   d. It permits experimentation that would be impractical or impossible in the real system.

10. Which of the following is not a special-purpose simulation language?
    a. GPSS
    b. SIMSCRIPT
    c. BASIC
    d. SLAM II

ANSWER KEY

Terms

1. D   3. F   5. A   7. J   9. E
2. I   4. H   6. G   8. B   10. C

Review Exercises

1. First develop the cumulative probability distribution for x and use it to assign random number blocks to the variable values.

x	p(x)	P(x)	Random Numbers
0	.05	.05	0 - .049999
1	.10	.15	.05 - .149999
2	.20	.35	.15 - .349999
3	.25	.60	.35 - .599999
4	.20	.80	.60 - .799999
5	.10	.90	.80 - .899999
6	.10	1.00	.90 - .999999

Take the first 10 values from the first column of Table 15.6 and match them to the x values.

Value	Random Number	x		Value	Random Number	x
1	.445282	3		6	.935282	6
2	.066257	1		7	.393437	3
3	.615352	4		8	.874742	5
4	.594821	3		9	.345906	2
5	.428152	3		10	.230927	2

2. Since the number of arrivals has a Poisson distribution, the time between arrivals follows an exponential distribution. The process generator for an exponential distribution is:

$$x = -(\frac{1}{\lambda})\ln(r)$$

where x is the time between consecutive arrivals, λ is the average rate of arrivals, and r is a random number from the range 0 to 1. Here $\lambda = 20$ per hour or 1/3 per minute. Thus, we will use:

$$x = -3 \ln(r)$$

Arrival	r	ln(r)	x	Arrival Time
1	–	–	–	9:00
2	.353333	−1.0403	3	9:03
3	.441906	−0.8167	2	9:05
4	.579120	−0.5462	2	9:07
5	.992685	−0.0073	0	9:07
6	.664736	−0.4084	1	9:08
7	.477204	−0.7398	2	9:10
8	.436322	−0.8294	2	9:12
9	.522334	−0.6494	2	9:14
10	.319852	−1.1409	3	9:17

3. To estimate the average waiting time, we need to find the total waiting time for the 10 cars. To find the percentage of utilization, we can find the total utilization during the time that 10 cars pass through the system (20 minutes) and divide it by the total elapsed time for the 10 cars.

First, we develop the process generator function table for the inter-arrival times.

Δt	$p(\Delta t)$	$P(\Delta t)$	Random Numbers
1	.15	.15	0 – .149999
2	.30	.45	.15 – .449999
3	.40	.85	.45 – .849999
4	.15	1.00	.85 – .999999

Car	r	Δt	Arrive	Start	End	Wait
1	–	–	0	0	2	0
2	.445282	2	2	2	4	0
3	.066257	1	3	4	6	1
4	.615352	3	6	6	8	0
5	.594821	3	9	9	11	0
6	.428152	2	11	11	13	0
7	.935282	4	15	15	17	0
8	.393437	2	17	17	19	0
9	.874724	4	21	21	23	0
10	.345906	2	23	23	25	0

Ten cars waited a total of 1 minute, so W_q = .1 minute. It took 25 minutes to provide 20 minutes of service for 10 cars, so the percentage of utilization is 20/25 = .80.

4. a. Given the information, λ = .5 per minute and μ = 2/3 per minute. This gives the two process generators:

Interarrival time = Δt = $(-2)\ln(r_1)$
Service time = s = $(-1.5)\ln(r_2)$

Customer	r_1	t	Arrival Time	Start Service	r_2	Service Time	End Service	Wait
-	-	-	-	0	.494758	1.1	1.1	-
-	-	-	-	1.1	.353555	1.6	2.7	-
-	-	-	0	1.6	.407208	1.3	4.0	-
1	.112460	4.4	4.4	4.4	.682154	.6	5.0	0
2	.055118	5.8	10.2	10.2	.827656	.3	10.5	0
3	.936548	.1	10.3	10.5	.379244	1.5	12.0	.2
4	.602720	1.0	11.3	12.0	.535109	.9	12.9	.7
5	.135047	4.0	15.3	15.3	.867939	.2	15.5	0
6	.445679	1.6	16.9	16.9	.957102	.1	17.0	0
7	.077000	5.1	22.0	22.0	.025220	5.5	27.5	0
8	.261491	2.7	24.7	27.5	.503207	1.0	28.5	2.8
9	.805962	.4	25.1	28.5	.571261	.8	29.3	3.4
10	.253941	2.7	27.8	29.3	.025378	5.5	34.8	1.5
11	.484498	1.4	29.2	34.8	.838279	.3	35.1	5.6
12	.282878	2.5	31.7	35.1	.281099	1.9	37.0	3.4
13	.214300	3.1	34.8	37.0	.679630	.6	37.6	2.2
14	.453834	1.6	36.4	37.6	.142509	2.9	40.5	1.2
15	.523906	1.3	37.7	40.5	.818984	.3	40.8	2.8
16	.754386	.6	38.3	40.8	.224342	2.2	43.0	2.5
17	.105069	4.5	42.8	43.0	.165914	2.7	45.7	.2
18	.503880	1.4	44.2	45.7	.095737	3.5	49.2	1.5
19	.355410	2.1	46.3	49.2	.038363	4.9	54.1	2.9
20	.125302	4.2	50.5	54.1	.195636	2.4	56.5	3.6

Total Waiting Time = 34.5 minutes
Average Waiting Time = 1.725 minutes per customer

b. The appropriate queuing theory model from Chapter 14 is the basic single-server model. For that model:

$$W_q = \lambda / [\mu(\mu-\lambda)]$$

For λ = .5 and μ = 2/3, we get:

$$W_q = .5/[.667(.667-.5)] = 4.5 \text{ minutes}$$

in comparison with the experimental average waiting time of 1.725 minutes.

5. The procedure involves two steps. First, we use a random number to determine the length of the delivery time in weeks. Second, we sample that many values from a Normal distribution with the given mean and standard distribution.

The process generator for delivery time is:

Delivery Time	Probability	Cumulative Probability	Random Numbers (r_1)
1	.20	.20	0 - .199999
2	.40	.60	.20 - .599999
3	.25	.85	.60 - .849999
4	.15	1.00	.85 - .999999

We get the weekly use value in the following way:

i)   Take a random number (r_2).
ii) Using the Normal distribution table in Appendix C, invert to find the Z value with cumulative probability given by the random number.
iii) Convert from Z to x by x = 1000 + 100Z.

Since the probabilities in Appendix C are given to four decimal places, we will round the random number to four places and then use the closest Z value.

a.

Delivery Period	r_1	Delivery Time	r_2	Z	Weekly Use	Total Use
1	.956412	4	.2856	-.57	943	
			.5696	1.08	1108	
			.4210	-.20	980	
			.8713	1.13	1113	4144
2	.625270	3	.0542	-1.61	839	
			.1729	-.94	906	
			.2899	-.55	945	2690
3	.014319	1	.3138	.49	1049	1049
4	.668440	3	.3198	.47	1047	
			.9681	1.85	1185	
			.4237	-.19	981	3213
5	.750516	3	.1486	-1.04	896	
			.1130	-1.21	879	
			.1265	-1.14	886	2661
6	.264349	2	.2988	-.53	947	
			.6132	.29	1029	1976
7	.517650	2	.1740	-.94	906	
			.9030	1.30	1130	2036
8	.854214	4	.8651	1.10	1110	
			.7134	.56	1056	
			.3380	-.42	948	
			.1870	-.89	911	4025
9	.488950	2	.0370	-1.79	821	
			.4337	-.17	983	1804
10	.865850	4	.7876	.80	1080	
			.5912	.23	1023	
			.1136	-1.21	879	
			.1742	-.94	906	3888

Based on the 10 values in the sample, we get $\bar{x}$ = 2748.6 and s = 1053.4 as our estimates of the mean and standard deviation of delivery time use.

b. With 1000 observations, calculate the mean and standard deviation. You can then apply either the Chi-square or the Kolmogorov-Smirnov test described in the text to test for a Normal distribution.

6. As discussed in the text, the process generator for the exponential distribution is:

$$x = -\left(\frac{1}{\lambda}\right) \ln(r)$$

where x is the variable of interest (in this case the time between failures for a given circuit), r is the random number in the range 0 to 1, and is the rate of occurrence of the event. In this case, $1/\lambda$ = 2500 hours, so the process generator is:

$$x = (-2500)\ln(r).$$

Since there are three circuits, there will be three identical generators. These three, with random numbers coming from columns 1, 2, and 3 of Table 15.6, have been used to generate sequences of circuit-life lengths which are given in the table below. These circuit lives form the basis for the three simulations, using the same lives in each simulation to reduce the comparison error.

<u>Randomly Determined Circuit Lives</u>

Circuit 1		Circuit 2		Circuit 3	
r_1	Life	r_2	Life	r_3	Life
.445282	2023	.353333	2601	.112460	5463
.066257	6786	.441906	2042	.055118	7246
.615352	1214	.579120	1366	.936548	164
.594821	1299	.992685	18	.602720	1266
.428152	2121	.664736	1021	.135047	5005
.935282	167	.447204	2012	.445679	2020
.393437	2332	.436322	2073	.077000	6410
.874724	335	.522334	1624	.261491	3353
.345906	2654	.319852	2850	.805962	539
.230927	3664	.722047	814	.253941	3427
.383484	2396	.155976	4645	.484498	1812
.866792	357	.680668	962	.282878	3157
.402887	2273	.806714	537	.214300	3851
.978072	55	.876081	331	.453834	1975
.376035	2445	.984704	39	.523906	1616
.608526	1242	.205187	3960	.754386	705
.987430	32	.165323	4500	.105069	5633
.588776	1324	.800478	556	.503880	1714
.916667	218	.434235	2085	.355410	2586
.399848	2292	.620655	1192	.125302	5193
.401840	2280	.177596	4321	.449017	2002

<u>Rule (i)</u>: Three separate simulations are run since there is no connection between circuit replacements unless there happens to be two or three that fail simultaneously. The three circuit simulations are shown in the table labelled for Rule (i) immediately below.

Simulation for Rule (i)

Circuit 1		Circuit 2		Circuit 3	
Life	Failure Time	Life	Failure Time	Life	Failure Time
2023	2023	2601	2601	5463	5463
6786	8809	2042	5003	7246	12709
1214	10023	1366	6369	164	12873
1299	11322	18	6387	1266	14139
2121	13443	1021	7408	5005	19144
167	13610	2012	9420		
2332	15942	2073	11493		
		1624	13117		
		2850	15967		

As can be readily seen, there are 18 total on-circuit replacements, six for Circuit 1, eight for Circuit 2, and four for Circuit 3, within the 15,000 hours. At $115 each, the cost is $2070.

Rule (ii): Rule (ii) calls for replacing any failed circuit and, in addition, any other circuit that is at least 2500 hours old. We will keep a record of time, noting when each failure is to take place, also noting at that time whether any other circuit is old enough to replace. Any replaced circuit will have a new life determined to establish when it would next fail. This is shown in the Rule (ii) simulation table. As we can see, there are 14 single replacements at $115 each and four double replacements at $180 each for a total cost of $2330.

Simulation for Rule (ii)

Time	Replace	Cost	Time of Next Failure		
			Ct. 1	Ct. 2	Ct. 3
0	All new	–	2023	2601	5463
2023	1*	115	8809	2601	5463
2601	2*,3	180	8809	5003	9847
5003	1,2*	180	6217	6369	9847
6217	1*,3	180	7516	6369	6381
6369	2*	115	7516	6387	6381
6381	3*	115	7516	6387	7647
6387	2*	115	7516	7408	7647
7408	2*	115	7516	9420	7647
7516	1*	115	7683	9420	7647
7647	3*	115	7683	9420	12652
7683	1*	115	10015	9420	12652
9420	2*	115	10015	11493	12652
10015	1*	115	10350	11493	12652
10350	1*,3	180	13004	11493	12370
11493	2*	115	13004	13117	12370
12370	3*	115	13004	13117	18780
13004	1*	115	16668	13117	18780
13117	2*	115	16668	15967	18780
15967	Past the end of the simulation				

*indicates a failure; ___ means next replacement time

212

Rule (iii): Each time there is a failure we replace all three circuits. Thus, every time there is a failure we take three new life values, one for each circuit, and use the smallest to determine when the next failure and triple replacement will take place. This is shown in the Rule (iii) simulation table below. The total cost of this policy is $4900 based on 20 replacements of all three circuits at $245 each time.

Simulation for Rule (iii)

Time	Failure	Ct. 1	New Lives Ct. 2	Ct. 3
0	–	2023	2601	5463
2023	1	6726	2042	7246
4065	2	1214	1366	164
4229	3	1299	18	1266
4247	2	2121	1021	5005
5268	2	167	2012	2020
5435	1	2332	2073	6410
7508	2	335	1624	3353
7843	1	2654	2850	539
8382	3	3664	814	3427
9196	2	2396	4645	1812
11008	3	357	962	3157
11365	1	2273	537	3851
11902	2	55	331	1975
11957	1	2445	39	1616
11996	2	1242	3960	705
12701	3	32	4500	5633
12733	1	1324	556	1714
13289	2	218	2085	2586
13507	1	2292	1192	5193
14699	2	2280	4321	2002
16701	Past the end of the simulation			

___ indicates the first to fail

Based on the simulation results, it appears that Rule (i), individual replacement, is best.

Chapter Test

1. c	3. b	5. c	7. d	9. b
2. a	4. d	6. d	8. c	10. c

CHAPTER SIXTEEN

INVENTORY SYSTEMS

MAIN POINTS

1. Inventory is material held for future production or sales. It may be raw material, work in progress, or finished goods.

2. Inventories are held to smooth production, to make sure goods are available for use or sale so as to meet customer demands, to balance holding versus set-up costs, to take advantage of quantity purchase discounts, and to guard against long or uncertain lead times.

3. Inventory models seek to minimize the total cost of the inventory system, which is the sum of ordering, carrying, and shortage costs.

4. Ordering costs are those involved in ordering or receiving inventory or, if the item is being produced, the costs of setting up a production run. These include personnel costs from purchasing, accounting, and receiving and purchase and transportation charges. Ordering costs are usually considered to be a fixed amount per order.

5. Carrying or holding costs are the direct and indirect costs of keeping stock. They include the cost of the money tied up in inventory, storage or warehousing costs, and the costs of obsolescence or spoilage. Carrying costs are usually expressed as a percentage of the value of a unit per time period.

6. Shortages or stockouts are of two types: backorders and lost sales. Both types incur record-keeping costs and the loss of customer goodwill. Lost sales also involve the lost profit on the sale not made. If the inventory is for internal use there are the costs of disrupted operations. Shortage costs are usually expressed as a cost per unit short per unit of time for backorders and a cost per unit for lost sales.

7. The two basic inventory control decisions are when to place an order and for how much. The appropriate decision procedure depends on whether demands are dependent or independent.

8. Dependent demand exists when the demand for one item is directly tied to the demand for another item. This is the case for the demands for components of a final product. A methodology for dealing with dependent demand items is material requirements planning (MRP).

9. The demands for final products, spare parts, and other items that are not being sold as part of something else are classified as independent. They are controlled with what are generally referred to as statistical inventory control models.

10. In order to allocate inventory control effort where it will do the most good, the first step is often an ABC classification, dividing items into three groups based on dollar use.

11. A physical or periodic review inventory system involves actually counting the inventory at specific points in time (the review period) to serve as the basis for ordering decisions.

12. In a continuous review system, the level of inventory is monitored constantly. Each item entered into or removed from inventory is recorded. This can be a simple manual system or a sophisticated computerized one, which may be either batch-processing or real-time. Real-time systems are the most sophisticated and up-to-date but are also the most expensive.

13. A computer-based inventory system may (at one extreme) only involve record-keeping or (at the other) actually decide on when and how much to order and prepare and send the purchase or production order. The most successful systems have been intermediate, with the computer suggesting orders for a human analyst to review and, if desired, modify.

14. The five steps in analyzing inventory problems are:
a. determine inventory system properties,
b. formulate an appropriate model,
c. solve or manipulate the model,
d. perform sensitivity analysis,
e. incorporate the model in the control system.

15. Inventory system properties relate to demands, replenishment, costs, and constraints.

16. Demand properties include the size, rate, and pattern of demand. Size and rate may be constant or variable, deterministic or stochastic.

17. One aspect of replenishment is the scheduling period, the time between replenishment decisions. This may be constant (periodic review) or variable (continuous review). Lead time is the time between placing and receiving an order. This may be fixed or variable and, if variable, either deterministic or stochastic.

18. Rather than using fixed, constant order quantities, the system may specify an order level, the desired quantity in inventory after replenishment. The actual quantity received may also be stochastic, differing from the amount ordered.

19. The replenishment pattern determines how an order is received. The order may be received all in one batch, in smaller batches spread over time, or in a stream over time.

20. Since system costs are generally estimates, the analyst must determine the sensitivity of decisions to minor variations in cost values.

21. Decisions may be constrained by any of a variety of factors. The more common ones are working capital, space, scheduling period, shortages, dependent demand, and whether demands can be treated as continuous or must be dealt with as discrete.

22. Inventory models are deterministic or stochastic. All features of deterministic models are assumed to be known. In stochastic models, some relevant features (generally demand and/or lead time) are probabilistic. Stochastic models are more difficult to analyze.

23. If a model cannot be solved analytically, simulation is a possibility. If possible, analysis is preferred since it costs less and yields an optimal solution. One must be careful, however, of developing an over-simplified model in order to make it solvable.

24. A sensitivity analysis can be performed on the model in order to determine how accurate the parameter estimates need to be.

25. Many inventory control models have developed since the first one in 1913. The first one, the basic economic order quantity (EOQ) model, is still one of the most popular and forms the basis for many other models.

26. Although the assumptions that characterize the system for which the basic EOQ model is appropriate are unrealistic, the model is widely used and successful in controlling inventory costs.

27. The basic EOQ model assumes that demand and all costs are known and constant over an infinite time horizon. Shortages are not permitted. Replenishment is of constant size and all-at-once with zero lead time.

28. The order quantity q* that minimizes the sum of ordering and holding costs for the basic EOQ model is:,

$$q* = (2C_3 r/C_1)^{1/2}$$

where r is the period usage rate, C_3 is the cost to place an order, and C_1 is the cost to hold one unit in inventory for one period.

29. The cost function for the basic EOQ model is fairly flat near q* so that using a value of q moderately different from the optimal will not have much effect on the cost. The q used may differ from q* because of errors in the parameters or because q* is not feasible. It may not be feasible if it is not a multiple of some standard delivery quantity.

30. There are many other relatively simple models based on dropping one or more of the assumptions of the basic EOQ model. Models presented cover: basic EOQ with finite replenishment rate, basic order level system with fixed review period, basic EOQ with discrete price breaks, and the basic EOQ with safety stock to handle stochastic lead time use.

31. More complex inventory systems can be examined with simulation, using the techniques of Chapter 15. The disadvantages of simulation are its cost and the fact that it is descriptive rather than optimizing. It presents, however, a way to test inventory control policies when the system cannot be modelled and solved analytically.

32. A procedure for controlling ordering and inventories of dependent demand items is material requirements planning (MRP). This situation is common in manufacturing. Dependent demand patterns tend to be irregular or lumpy which make the basic EOQ model and its variations inappropriate.

33. The objective of MRP is to get the right material in the right place at the right time.

34. MRP is actually a data-processing system rather than a theoretical inventory model like the basic EOQ model. It requires a computer for the huge amounts of computation. Successful MRP systems coordinate not only inventory but also purchasing and manufacturing.

35. MRP is based on calculating the demand for component parts based on the demands for the final products they go into rather than forecasting their needs.

36. The implementation of a successful MRP system requires a realistic master production schedule, accurate bills of material, accurate inventory files, known lead times, and unique part numbers for all items.

37. A master production schedule is a period-by-period (usually weekly) plan of what final products are to be produced. It is usually firm in the near future and flexible further out.

38. A bill of materials (BOM) is a structured listing of all component parts, showing how (structurally, not technologically) they are put together into higher level assemblies and, eventually, into the final product.

39. MRP works by scheduling backwards, starting with the product's due date and then scheduling the earlier production of component parts to allow for lead time.

40. An MRP system not only provides initial schedules for production, but also reschedules open orders to reflect changes in due dates and the availability of other required parts.

41. Computers have become extremely important for inventory control systems in keeping accurate, timely records, making decisions about ordering, and operating MRP systems.

42. Two potentially serious problems in using inventory models are: (1) the misapplication of models in situations where their assumptions are not met, and (2) the failure to consider the willingness of the people involved to accept a new system.

SUGGESTED READINGS

Selected applications are:

Brout, D. B., "Scientific Management of Inventory on a Hand-held Calculator," Interfaces, v. 11, n. 6 (December 1981), pp. 57-69.

Canel, A. G. and R. D. Galvao, "An Application of ABC Analysis to Control Imported Material," Interfaces, v. 10, n. 4 (August 1980), pp. 22-24.

Fincke, U. and W. Vaessen, "Reducing Distribution Costs in a Two-Level Inventory System at Ciba-Geigy," Interfaces, v. 18, n .6, (November-December 1988), pp. 92-104.

Gardner, E. S., Jr., "A Top-Down Approach to Modeling U. S. Navy Inventories," Interfaces, v. 17, n. 4 (July-August 1987), pp. 1-7.

Liberatore, M. J., "Using MRP and EOQ/Safety Stock for Raw Materials Inventory Control: Discussion and Case Study," Interfaces, v. 9, n. 2, Part 1 (April 1979), pp. 1-7.

Steinberg, E., W. B. Lee, and B. M. Khumawala, "MRP Applications in the Space Program," Production and Inventory Management, v. 23, n. 2 (Second Quarter 1982), pp. 65-77.

KEY TERMS

Match each term with the appropriate definition below.

Terms

_____ 1. ABC classification

_____ 2. bill of materials

_____ 3. continuous review system

_____ 4. demand pattern

_____ 5. dependent demand

_____ 6. EOQ

_____ 7. independent demand

_____ 8. inventory

_____ 9. lead time

_____ 10. lot size

_____ 11. master production schedule

_____ 12. MRP

_____ 13. order level

_____ 14. physical inventory system

_____ 15. replenishment

_____ 16. replenishment period

_____ 17. scheduling period

_____ 18. stock-out

Definitions

A. The time from placing to receiving an order.

B. The order quantity that minimizes total inventory system costs.

C. The receipt of an order.

D. The occurrence of demand when there is no inventory available to fill it.

E. The division of inventory items into groups based on value used during a year or other period.

F. The way in which orders are placed on the inventory system.

G. The time between review for placing an order.

H. A structured listing of the component parts of a product.

I. The desired amount of inventory after the receipt of an order.

J.   Demand for an item that cannot be tied directly to the demand for some
     other item.

K.   The time during which an order is received.

L.   An inventory record system in which all additions to and deletions from
     inventory are recorded.

M.   The amount of an item purchased or made as the result of one order.

N.   Material held for future use.

O.   A plan for the production of final products, listed for several time
     periods.

P.   Demand for an item that is derived directly from the demand for some
     other item.

Q.   An inventory control system based on periodic physical counting of inven-
     tory to make ordering decisions.

R.   A production and inventory control system designed for dependent demand
     items.

SOLVED PROBLEM

A local manufacturer uses a high-strength fastener in one of its production
processes at a fairly constant rate of 3,000 per month. They currently place
a purchase order each month for these fasteners. It costs $25 to place and
receive an order. The annual carrying cost has been determined to be thirty
percent of unit cost ($0.10 per fastener). Lead time is two weeks
(constant).

a.   What are the current relevant inventory costs?

b.   What order quantity should be used?

c.   How much would this save over the current order quantity?

d.   How frequently should an order be placed?

Solution

a.   Since the demand and lead time are both constant, the only inventory
     costs to be considered will be the carrying and ordering costs. There-
     fore, the current inventory costs will be:

$$C(q) = C_1(q/2) + C_3(r/q)$$

     The current order quantity, q, is one month's usage, or 3,000 units. The
     annual demand, r, is (3000)(12) = 36,000 units. The carrying cost, C_1,
     is (.30)(.10) = $0.03 per unit per year and the ordering cost, C_3, is
     $25.

$$C(3000) = .03(3000/2) + 25(36000/3000)$$
$$= 45 + 300$$
$$= 345.00$$

Note that the annual carrying costs are $45 and the annual ordering costs are $300. At the optimal order quantity, these costs should be equal. Since the annual ordering cost is higher than the annual carrying cost, we are likely ordering too frequently.

b. To find the optimal order quantity, the basic economic order quantity (EOQ) model should be used.

$$q^* = (2C_3 r/C_1)^{1/2} = [2(25)(36000)/.03]^{1/2} = 7746$$

An order of 7,746 units should be placed each order period. Of course, fasteners are likely to come in standard container sizes (e.g., 1,000 fasteners per case), so it may be impossible to order exactly 7,746 fasteners. Due to the insensitivity of this model, however, rounding this value should not incur a large incremental cost.

c. The annual inventory cost using the EOQ is:

$$C(7746) = .03(7746/2) + 25(36000/7746)$$
$$= 116.19 + 116.19$$
$$= 232.38$$

The annual carrying cost now equals the annual ordering cost. The savings over the current ordering policy are 345.00 - 232.38 = $112.62, a savings of 32.6 percent. If we were to round the EOQ to 8,000 units, the annual inventory cost would become $232.50, obviously a minimal cost over the optimal.

d. Orders would need to be placed every 7746/3000 = 2.58 months.

REVIEW EXERCISES

1. Edison Appliance Co. makes toasters. One component of these toasters is a "doneness" sensor that causes the toast to pop up and the toaster to shut off. Edison expects to use 600,000 of these per year at a reasonably constant rate. The sensors cost $0.75 each. It costs $40 for Edison to place and receive an order. They use an annual inventory carrying cost rate of 30 percent. Stockouts are not permitted. Lead time is fixed at one week and the order is received in one batch.

   What is the EOQ for this item? What is the average annual inventory system cost associated with it?

2. The sensors (Question 1) are sold in cases of 6,000. Recognizing this, what order quantity should Edison use? What is the effect on system cost?

3. The sensor supplier has offered Edison a discount of $.03 per sensor if they will buy 20 cases (120,000 units) at a time. Is this discount economically advantageous to Edison?

4. Another component of the toaster is the shell, stamped from a piece of chromed sheet steel. The stamping department can turn out shells at the rate of 75,000 per month. A shell costs $1.30 to make. It costs $62 to set up the equipment and issue a production order. The same 30 percent annual holding rate is used.

How many stamped shells should be made in each production run? How many runs will be made each year? How long will a production run last? Assume 250 working days per year.

*5. The demand for a particular item is fairly even at 1000 units per year. It costs $40 to place an order and $2.00 to keep one unit in inventory for a year. Assuming a 50-week year, the average use per week is 20 units. The standard deviation of use per week is 4 units. Weekly use is Normally distributed and independent from week to week.

If the lead time is 2 weeks, what should the reorder point and order quantity be if the company is willing to accept a stockout on an average of once every two years?

6. A stereo equipment store uses a reorder point system for controlling inventories. The demand for a particular stereo unit averages approximately 10 units per week. It costs $50 to place and receive an order. The carrying cost on a stereo unit is $90 per year. The profit on a unit is $60. The store is open 52 weeks per year. Delivery from the supplier takes one week.

What order quantity and reorder point should the store use for this stereo unit? The probability distribution for demand per week is:

Demand	Probability
0	.1
5	.2
10	.4
15	.2
20	.1

7. The Barrow Co. makes wheelbarrows, among other things. One particular wheelbarrow model is composed of parts as shown in the diagram.

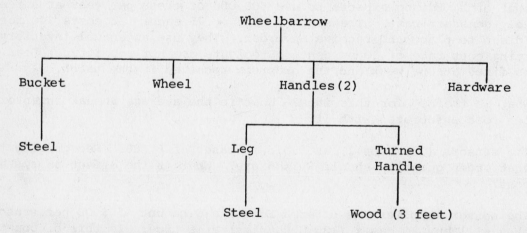

It takes one week to assemble the bucket, wheel, handles, and hardware together into a wheelbarrow. Assembling the turned handle and leg piece

222

together takes one week. It takes two weeks to cut, turn and drill the wood to make turned handles. It requires two weeks to receive the wood from the mill. If there is an order for 200 wheelbarrows to be delivered in week 10, when should wood be ordered from the mill and in what quantity? Assume that there is no wood presently available in the factory.

CHAPTER TEST

1. The issues involved in developing inventory control models apply to:
   a. raw materials.
   b. work in process.
   c. finished goods.
   d. all of the above.

2. In the basic EOQ model the cost of an individual unit:
   a. has no effect.
   b. enters through the ordering cost.
   c. determines the carrying cost.
   d. none of the above.

3. When using the basic EOQ model, if the annual use were to double, the optimal order quantity would:
   a. not change.
   b. increase by the square root of 2.
   c. double.
   d. quadruple.

4. Which of the following is not a concern in developing or selecting an inventory control model?
   a. Dependent vs. independent demand.
   b. Cost characteristics.
   c. Replenishment characteristics.
   d. None of the above.

5. If the inventory control policy is based on checking the actual inventory level at selected points in time to determine whether and how much to order, the system is classified as:
   a. a continuous review system.
   b. a periodic review system.
   c. an order level system.
   d. a replenishment period system.

6. Which of the following is not a characteristic of the basic EOQ model?
   a. Known and constant demand.
   b. Constant costs.
   c. Limited storage space.
   d. Infinite replenishment rate.

7. For which of the following items would a dependent demand inventory control system be appropriate?
   a. Wheels for a wagon.
   b. Aspirin for a hospital.
   c. Lubricating oil for a machine.
   d. Stamps for an office.

8. Which of the following is <u>not</u> generally considered to be part of the carrying cost?
   a. The interest on the money.
   b. The wages in the receiving department.
   c. The warehouse rental.
   d. All are.

9. A continuous review inventory control system:
   a. works well for dependent demand items.
   b. must be operated with a computer.
   c. only keeps track of the use of the item.
   d. requires recording all receipts and uses.

10. The types of costs generally considered in an inventory control system are:
    a. ordering, carrying, and shortage.
    b. ordering, shortage, and unit purchase.
    c. shortage, lead time, and receiving.
    d. ordering, carrying, and production.

ANSWER KEY

Key Terms

1. E	5. P	9. A	13. I	17. G
2. H	6. B	10. M	14. Q	18. D
3. L	7. J	11. O	15. C	
4. F	8. N	12. R	16. K	

Review Exercises

1. The conditions are met for using the basic EOQ model.

   $r = 600,000/\text{year}$, $C_3 = \$40/\text{order}$, $C_1 = .30(.75) = .225/\text{unit/year}$

   $$q^* = (2C_3 r/C_1)^{1/2} = [2(40)(600,000)/.225]^{1/2} = 14,606 \text{ units}$$

   $$C(q^*) = 40(\frac{600000}{14606}) + .225(\frac{14606}{2}) = 1643.16 + 1643.18 = \$3286.34$$

2. Since $q^* = 14,606$, the optimal order quantity with the batch size restriction will be one of the multiples of 6000 that bracket q^*, either 12,000 or 18,000. Try both to see which has the lower cost.

   $$C(12000) = 40(\frac{600000}{12000}) + .225(\frac{12000}{2}) = 2000 + 1350 = \$3350$$

   $$C(18000) = 40(\frac{600000}{18000}) + .225(\frac{18000}{2}) = 1333.33 + 2025 = \$3358.33$$

   Since $C(12,000) < C(18,000)$, Edison should order in lots of size 12,000. The cost will be $3350 per year, an increase of 1.9 percent above the optimum.

3. The conditions are met for applying the basic EOQ model with price discounts. There are two prices:

224

If q $<$ 120,000, b_1 = \$.75.

If q $\geq$ 120,000, b_2 = \$.72.

Starting with b_2 = \$.72, find the EOQ for each price and compare their costs.

$\underline{b_2 = \$0.72}$

C_1 = .30(.72) = .216

q^* = $[2(40)(600,000)/.216]^{1/2}$ = 14,907

Since this is $<$ 120,000, EOQ_2 = 120,000.

C(120000) = 40(600000/120000) + .216(120000/2) + .72(600000)
   = 200 + 12,960 + 432,000 = \$445,160

$\underline{b_1 = \$0.75}$

We already know that the EOQ is 12,000 units (Question 2). The cost of ordering and holding inventory is \$3350 to which we add the purchase cost of .75(600,000). The total cost is thus \$453,350. Edison can save \$8,190 per year by buying in lots of size 120,000 or 20 cases at a time. Whether Edison should do so or not in view of the extra space and the substantially larger cash flow required is another matter.

4. The conditions are met to apply the basic EOQ with finite replenishment model. For this model:

$$q^* = \frac{(2rC_3/C_1)^{1/2}}{(1 - r/p)^{1/2}}$$

r = 600,000 per year = 50,000 per month
p = 75,000 per month
C_3 = \$62 C_1 = .30(1.30) = .39

$$q^* = \frac{[2(600,000)(62)/.39]^{1/2}}{(1 - 50,000/75,000)^{1/2}} = 23,923$$

With 250 working days per year, the stamping department turns out 3,600 units per day. 23,923 units would take 6.65 days to produce. There would be 25.1 production runs per year on average. In practice, the production lot size would probably be rounded off to an even multiple of a day's work, such as 7 days, which would give a production lot size of 25,200 units.

5. First, find the optimal order quantity using the basic EOQ model.
     r = 1000 C_1 = 2.00 C_3 = 40

$$q^* = (2rC_3/C_1)^{1/2} = [2(40)(1000)/2]^{1/2} = 200 \text{ units}$$

This means that there will be five order cycles per year. One stockout every other year is then one stockout per every 10 cycles or a stockout probability of .10 on a single cycle. The reorder point should be set so that the probability that demand during the lead time exceeds the reorder point is .10.

The probability distribution of demand during a week is Normal with μ = 20 and σ = 4, independent from week to week. The demand during a two-week lead time is the sum of the two weekly demands. The expected value of the sum of independent variables is tee sum of their expected values. The variance of the sum of independent variables is the sum of their variances. Thus, if d is the demand during the lead time, we have:

$$\mu_d = \mu_1 + \mu_2 = 20 + 20 = 40$$

$$\sigma_d = (\sigma_1^2 + \sigma_2^2)^{1/2} = (16 + 16)^{1/2} = (32)^{1/2} = 5.66$$

Lead time demand thus has an expected value of 40 and a standard deviation of 5.66 and is normally distributed.

We need to find the reorder point value ROP for which:

$$P(d > ROP) = .10$$

The Z value with probability .10 to the right is 1.28 (Table in Appendix C). Thus:

$$ROP = \mu_d + Z\sigma_d = 40 + 1.28(5.66) = 47.2$$

The expected use during the lead time is 40 units. The safety stock is 7.2 units.

6. Based on the expected use, ordering cost, and holding cost, the optimal order quantity is:

$$q^* = (2(50)(520)/90)^{1/2} = 24 \text{ units}$$

The reorder point should be set so as to balance the expected stockout and holding costs.

ROP = 0:

$$C_2 = [0(.1)(60) + 5(.2)(60) + 10(.4)(60) \\ + 15(.2)(60) + 20(.1)(60)](520/24) = \$13{,}000$$

$$\Delta C_1 = 0$$

ROP = 5:

$$C_2 = [0(.1)(60) + (0)(.2)(60) + 5(.4)(60) \\ + 10(.2)(60) + 15(.1)(60)](520/24) = \$7{,}150$$

$$\Delta C_1 = 5(.1)(90) = \$45$$

ROP = 10:

$$C_2 = [0(.1)(60) + (0)(.2)(60) + 0(.4)(60) \\ + 5(.2)(60) + 10(.1)(60)](520/24) = \$1{,}950$$

$$\Delta C_1 = 10(.1)(90) + 5(.2)(90) = \$180$$

ROP = 15:

$$C_2 = [0(.1)(60) + (0)(.2)(60) + 0(.4)(60) \\ + 0(.2)(60) + 5(.1)(60)](520/24) = \$650$$

$$\Delta C_1 = 15(.1)(90) + 10(.2)(90) + 5(.4)(90) = \$495$$

ROP = 20:

$$C_2 = 0$$

$$\Delta C_1 = 20(.1)(90) + 15(.2)(90) + 10(.4)(90) + 5(.2)(90) + 0(.1)(90) \\ = \$900$$

ROP	C_2	ΔC_1	Total Cost
0	$13,000	$ 0	$13,000
5	7,150	45	7,195
10	1,950	180	2,130
15	650	495	1,145
20	0	900	900*

They should use a reorder point of 20 units.

7. To assemble the wheelbarrows for week 10, the component parts must be available for week 9 (one week assembly time). So they need 400 handles (two per wheelbarrow) in week 9. Taking one week to assemble the handle means the turned handles must be available in week 8. It takes two weeks to convert three feet of wood into a turned handle, so 1200 feet of wood must be there in week 6. Giving two weeks for delivery, they should order 1200 feet of wood in week 4.

Chapter Test

1. d	3. b	5. b	7. a	9. d
2. c	4. d	6. c	8. b	10. a

CHAPTER SEVENTEEN

DECISION SUPPORT SYSTEMS

MAIN POINTS

1. A decision support system (DSS) is a computer-based system with decision-making or decision-aiding capability. It goes beyond simply providing the decision maker with relevant and timely information.

2. The basic components of a DSS are a data base, information processing software, and appropriate decision models. Besides the standard reports generally available from more limited management information systems (MIS), a DSS often provides daily operating decisions and answers to more complex "what-if" questions.

3. A DSS can be looked at as the overlap or marriage of MIS and OR/MS, containing elements or characteristics of both.

4. OR/MS applications involve two general areas: decision oriented applications, which are generally one-time, nonrecurring decisions, and decision process applications, relating to the procedures for making recurring decisions. A DSS can be applied to both areas.

5. A DSS often has four modules. A <u>front-end processor</u> interacts with <u>data bases</u> to extract needed data and manipulate it. The data is processed by statistical or management science <u>models</u> to provide analysis or suggested decisions which are processed by a <u>back-end processor</u> that translates the outputs into a user-friendly format.

6. Information systems have evolved rapidly in the past 20 years, progressing through progressively more sophisticated and computerized stages. The basic system stages are: manual transaction processing, electronic accounting machines, computer-based transaction processing, MIS, and, finally, DSS. Transaction reporting systems are not decision-oriented but record relevant inputs, check for errors, and provide control reports. An MIS goes beyond this to provide information for decision making, providing information retrieval and report preparation. A DSS incorporates decision models and supports a wider range of less structured problem solving, providing the capability of incorporating human judgment in problem identification, data selection, model building and selection, and solution evaluation.

7. The basic characteristics of a DSS are:
   a. designed to support decision making,
   b. interactive to allow fast access to models and data,
   c. flexible to satisfy needs and styles of many styles and levels of managers,
   d. integrated set of models and data to avoid suboptimization,
   e. dynamic enough to keep itself up to date, and
   f. sophisticated, using modern information processing and OR/MS techniques.

8. The three major subsystems of a DSS are the database, the decision models, and the decision maker. The <u>database</u> contains data from both internal and external sources. The <u>decision models</u> support all management levels, top, middle, and lower, requiring communication linkages to avoid suboptimization. The <u>decision maker</u> must have the capability of interacting with all system components, using a <u>command language</u> to direct system activities.

9. Desirable design criteria for a DSS are:
    a. CRT terminals for communication,
    b. the ability to compare the system status with goals,
    c. an English-like database management system for interactive access, and
    d. real-time and on-line decision-maker control.

10. A DSS provides the capability for man/machine dialogs to provide on-line situation structuring and model building. This permits the expansion of OR/MS to become more flexible and provide the technology to support the process of exploring/structuring, interpreting, and implementing.

11. The benefits of DSS should be:
    a. decreased time and cost of decision making,
    b. increased applicability and efficiency of structuring managerial situations, and
    c. improved collaboration between managers and analysts.

12. The implementation of DSS remains slow due to:
    a. lack of understanding by managers of what can be expected,
    b. lack of system designer motivation,
    c. lack of designer expertise,
    d. human and system inertia, and
    e. the increased risk of failure of more complex systems.

13. A DSS should be designed and implemented because it can aid a manager in making better, more cost-effective decisions. The impetus to development should come from managers, DP professionals, and OR/MS professionals.

14. Developments in both hardware and software enhance the prospects for DSS development. New user-friendly software and widely distributed and networked microcomputers will encourage the distribution of DSS in large organizations and make them accessible to small ones.

SUGGESTED READINGS

Selected applications are:

Adelman, L, "Real-Time Computer Support for Decision Analysis in a Group Setting: Another Class of Decision Support Systems," <u>Interfaces</u>, v. 14, n. 2 (April 1984), pp. 75-83.

Bell, W. J., "Improving the Distribution of Industrial Gases with an On-line Computerized Routing and Scheduling Optimizer," <u>Interfaces</u>, v. 13, n. 6 (December 1983), pp. 4-23.

Roy, A., E. E. DeFalomir, and L. Lasdon, "An Optimization-Based Decision Support System for a Product Mix Problem," Interfaces, v. 12, n. 2 (April 1982), pp. 26-33.

Sauder, R. L. and W. M. Westerman, "Computer Aided Train Dispatching: Decision Support Through Optimization," Interfaces, v. 13, n. 6 (December 1983), pp. 24-37.

KEY TERMS

Match each term with the appropriate definition below.

Terms

_____ 1. command language

_____ 2. database

_____ 3. decision support system

_____ 4. information

_____ 5. information retrieval

_____ 6. real-time

_____ 7. transaction processing system

Definitions

A. Data which has been manipulated and organized to serve as the basis for decision making.

B. A system for recording events of importance to an organization.

C. An easy-to-use computer language that facilitates access to databases, the development and display of information, and the use of decision models.

D. The process of recovering information from a data base.

E. An integrated man/machine system incorporating databases and decision support models.

F. An integrated collection of files providing the data to support decision making.

G. Referring to the access to computer files and the outputs from decision modules as the manager requires them.

CHAPTER TEST

1. Which of the following statements would not be true of a decision support system?
   a. It is computer based.
   b. It has decision making capabilities.
   c. It helps in structuring managerial problems.
   d. All are true.

2. Which of the following would not be classified as transactions for a transaction processing system?
    a. Sales.
    b. Purchases
    c. Ordering decisions.
    d. Inventory withdrawals.

3. Which of the following statements would not be a characteristic of a transaction processing system?
    a. It is decision oriented.
    b. It provides error reports.
    c. It provides basic accounting performance reports.
    d. All are characteristics of a transaction processing system.

4. The decision models subsystem should support decision making by managers at which level of an organization?
    a. Top.
    b. Middle.
    c. Lower.
    d. All levels.

5. The decision maker's ability to interact with the components of a DSS is provided by the:
    a. interactive capability.
    b. command language.
    c. on-line access.
    d. decision models subsystem.

6. Which of the following characteristics is not a general one of decision support systems?
    a. Interactive.
    b. Supports decision making.
    c. Sophisticated.
    d. All are.

7. Which of the following would not be considered as a likely output of a DSS relating to the inventory system of a company?
    a. A monthly inventory status report.
    b. A list of recommended purchases for the next week.
    c. A study to determine the cost of carrying inventory.
    d. A study on the effects of changing the inventory ordering rules.

8. Which of the following would be classified as a decision oriented application for a DSS?
    a. The determination of the location of a new product distribution center.
    b. The determination of the allocation of monthly output to distribution centers.
    c. The determination of the number of room reservations a hotel should accept for a particular night.
    d. The development of a production-inventory-workforce plan for the next six months.

9. Which of the following would be classified as a decision process application for a DSS?
   a. The decision on whether to contract maintenance for equipment or perform it oneself.
   b. The development of an equipment replacement policy for an interstate trucking company.
   c. The determination of whether to move corporate headquarters.
   d. The decision as to whether to decentralize the inventory system.

10. The purpose of a "back-end processor" in a DSS is to:
    a. make output more intelligible to the user.
    b. make sure the output is correct.
    c. provide access to the data base.
    d. make decision suggestions.

ANSWER KEY

Key Terms

1. C	3. E	5. D	7. B
2. F	4. A	6. G	

Chapter Test

1. d	3. a	5. b	7. c	9. b
2. c	4. d	6. d	8. a	10. a

CHAPTER EIGHTEEN

HEURISTICS, AI, AND EXPERT SYSTEMS

MAIN POINTS

1. Heuristics play an important role in the solution of many problems in OR/MS. They are also the basis of many approaches in AI such as heuristic search and expert systems.

2. There are two primary reasons why heuristics are used in OR/MS: (1) the problem is too large or complex and can not be solved by an optimization method, and (2) the problem can be optimized, but a heuristic can yield a very effective solution that is much easier to obtain and more cost beneficial.

3. Examples of heuristics in OR/MS include VAM and the row minimum rule, the greedy algorithm, MINSLK, nearest neighbor, and the Silver-Meal heuristic.

4. The field of AI is rapidly growing as a discipline that can help solve certain kinds of qualitative or less well structured decision problems. AI involves more symbolic reasoning techniques as opposed to the numerical techniques of OR/MS.

5. AI is concerned with creating behavior by a machine or computer system that, if performed by a human, would be called intelligent.

6. The major applications of AI are:
   a. expert systems,
   b. natural language processors,
   c. computer vision/sensory systems,
   d. robotics, and
   e. speech recognition.

7. The two areas of AI that have had the most impact are expert systems and natural language processors.

8. An expert system is a system that employs human knowledge captured in a computer to solve problems that ordinarily require human expertise.

9. Knowledge engineering is the process of capturing or extracting knowledge from experts and other sources and representing that knowledge in a computer system.

10. Production type expert systems are composed of:
    a. a knowledge base consisting of production rules,
    b. a database of facts,
    c. an inference engine for reasoning and interpreting,
    d. an explanation mechanism to answer how and why questions, and
    e. a set of control strategies.

11. The main application areas of expert systems at this time are:
    a. diagnosis/categorization,
    b. design, and
    c. planning.

12. Expert or knowledge based systems are proliferating, but the vast majority are inferior to human experts. Additionally, they are applicable to a very narrow problem domain. A few of the true expert systems such as XCON rival human experts and offer significantly improved productivity and response times.

13. Combining OR/MS and AI techniques can lead to a more intelligent computer based system. Such a system could be called an intelligent DSS and could offer new levels of capability in dealing with various decision problems.

SUGGESTED READINGS

Selected applications are:

Andriole, S. J., ed., <u>Applications in Artificial Intelligence</u>, (Princeton, N. J.: Petrocelli Books, 1984).

Bachant, J. and J. McDermott, "R1 Revisited: Four Years in the Trenches," <u>AI Magazine</u>, v. 5, n. 3 (Fall 1984).

Fox, M. S. and S. F. Smith, "ISIS - A Knowledge-Based System for Factory Scheduling," <u>Expert Systems</u>, v. 1, n. 1 (1984).

Goyal, S. K., et. al., "COMPASS: An Expert System for Telephone Switch Maintenance," <u>Expert Systems</u>, (July 1985).

O'Shea, T. and M. Eisenstadt, <u>Artificial Intelligence: Tools, Techniques and Applications</u>, (New York: Harper and Row, 1984).

Simon, H. A., "Two Heads are Better than One: The Collaboration Between AI and OR," <u>Interfaces</u>, v. 17, n. 4 (July-August 1987), pp. 8-15.

KEY TERMS

Match each term with the appropriate definition below.

<u>Terms</u>

_____ 1. artificial intelligence

_____ 2. expert system

_____ 3. heuristic

_____ 4. inference engine

_____ 5. intelligent DSS

_____ 6. knowledge base

_____ 7. knowledge engineering

_____ 8. natural language processor

Definitions

A. The discipline whereby knowledge is integrated into a computer system in order to solve problems normally requiring human expertise.

B. The subfield of computer science that is concerned with symbolic reasoning and problem solving via machines.

C. Informal judgmental knowledge that consists of a rule or rules for solving a particular problem.

D. A computer based system that incorporates not only models and OR/MS methods but also AI techniques.

E. A user interface that allows the user to carry on a conversation with a computer based system in much the same way as he or she would converse with another human.

F. A computer system that achieves levels of performance in task areas that for human beings requires years of training or experience.

G. A set of rules, heuristics, and facts containing knowledge about a particular problem domain.

H. The component of an expert system that provides the reasoning, control, and interpretation capabilities.

CHAPTER TEST

1. Which of the following is <u>not</u> a reason to use a heuristic in solving a problem?
   a. low cost.
   b. guaranteed optimal solution.
   c. efficiency.
   d. ease of understanding.

2. Which of the following is <u>not</u> a component of a commercial expert system?
   a. knowledge base.
   b. inference engine.
   c. user interface.
   d. knowledge engineer.

3. Most expert systems capture knowledge in the form of:
   a. production rules.
   b. semantic nets.
   c. frames.
   d. objects.

4. Which phrase(s) best describes the role of a knowledge engineer?
   a. production.
   b. extraction.
   c. inference.
   d. assimilation.
   e. a and c.
   f. b and d.

5. Which of the following is <u>not</u> a major application area of AI?
   a. robotics.
   b. speech recognition.
   c. problem definition.
   d. computer vision.

6. Which of the following is <u>not</u> a characteristic of AI problem solving?
   a. strictly numerical computations.
   b. defies the mathematics of optimization.
   c. admits ill-specified goals.
   d. does symbolic reasoning.

7. Which of the following is <u>not</u> a heuristic described in the textbook?
   a. VAM.
   b. Row minimum.
   c. MINSLK.
   d. Greedy.
   e. None of the above.

8. Which of the following is <u>not</u> a primary discipline in AI?
   a. linguistics.
   b. electrical engineering.
   c. OR/MS.
   d. computer science.
   e. accounting.

9. Which of the following are software tools used extensively in the development of AI systems?
   a. LISP.
   b. PROLOG.
   c. FORTRAN.
   d. COBOL.
   e. a and b.
   f. c and d.

10. Which of the following best describes the best reason for the collaboration between OR and AI?
   a. Cost reductions in system development.
   b. The creation of computer-based systems that can replace experts.
   c. The creation of intelligent support systems that can often improve levels of suggestion and understanding.
   d. The creation of huge economic benefits for AI system vendors.
   e. All of the above.

ANSWER KEY

Key Terms

1. B	3. C	5. D	7. A
2. F	4. H	6. G	8. E

Chapter Test

1. b	3. a	5. c	7. e	9. e
2. d	4. f	6. a	8. e	10. c